An Illustrated Guide to the
STICK AND LEAF INSECTS
of Peninsular Malaysia and Singapore

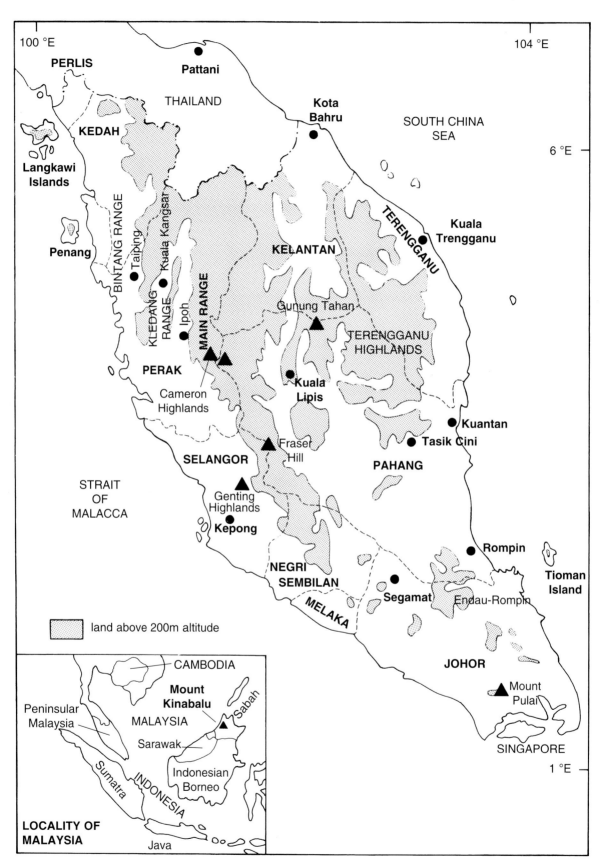

Map of Peninsular Malaysia and Singapore.

An Illustrated Guide to the
STICK AND LEAF INSECTS
of Peninsular Malaysia and Singapore

Francis Seow-Choen

with illustrations by the author

Natural History Publications (Borneo)
Kota Kinabalu

2000

Published by

Natural History Publications (Borneo) Sdn. Bhd.
A913, 9th Floor, Wisma Merdeka
P.O. Box 13908
88846 Kota Kinabalu, Sabah, Malaysia
Tel: 6088-233098 Fax: 6088-240768
e-mail: chewlun@tm.net.my

First published 2000.

An Illustrated Guide to the Stick and Leaf Insects
of Peninsular Malaysia and Singapore
    by Francis Seow-Choen

Layout and design by Cheng Jen Wai.

Frontispiece: Map of Peninsular Malaysia and Singapore.

Perpustakaan Negara Malaysia   Cataloguing-in-Publication Data

Seow-Choen, Francis
    An illustrated guide to the stick and leaf insects of Peninsular
    Malaysia and Singapore / Francis Seow-Choen ; with
    illustrations by the author.
    Bibliography: p. 166
    ISBN 983-812-029-4
    1. Stick insects—Semenanjung Malaysia. 2. Stick insects—
    Singapore. 3. Phasmidae—Semenanjung Malaysia.
    4. Phasmidae—Singapore. I. Title.
    595.729

Printed in Malaysia.

Contents

Introduction

The earliest Malayan* species of phasmids to be described were *Marmessoidea rosea* (Fabricius) in 1793 and *Heteropteryx dilatata* (Parkinson) in 1798. These were known respectively as *Mantis rosea* and *Phasma dilatatum* then. By 1835, Gray was able to publish his "Synopsis of Phasmidae", wherein, 134 species and several doubtful species were described. The first major text to illustrate phasmids was that of Westwood in 1859, where 471 species were described together with 48 black and white plates of illustrations. Stål in 1875 published his work on phasmid classification. Kirby in 1904 published his Catalogue of Phasmidae which included all references and type specimens deposited in the British Museum of Natural History in London up until 1904. The very voluminous monograph "Die Insektenfamilie Phasmiden" was published in three parts between 1906 and 1908 by Brunner von Wattenwyl and Redtenbacher recognising 1899 species. Karny revised the classification of phasmids in 1923 and despite being the most comprehensive taxonomic effort up till that time, still contained a fair amount of invalid name changes. The more recent times have seen a resurgence in interest in phasmids, resulting in the publication of many important papers on these insects. Nonetheless whilst South-east Asia has a large number of phasmids, very few local naturalists have done any work on these insects until very recently. The first book solely dedicated to tropical phasmids, entitled "A guide to the Stick and Leaf Insects of Singapore" by Seow-Choen was published in 1997. Brock published his authoritative monograph on *Phasmids of West Malaysia and Singapore* in 1999 whilst Philip Bragg will be doing the same for East Malaysian phasmids by publishing his PhD thesis. Brock recognised 102 species from West Malaysia and Singapore. Brock, although, listing *Carausius incertus* in his book did not number this species amongst the West Malaysian species, indicating that it may be an erroneous record. Furthermore, although listed by Brock in his book, *Marmessoidea rubescens* is an East Malaysian and not a West Malaysian species. Except for Seow-Choen's work, these latter books may be difficult to use in the field and especially for amateurs without entomological training. In addition, there continued to be the discovery of new species in these countries. There was, therefore, a need for another book on South-East Asian phasmids. The present book hopes to fill this gap. It is hoped that this illustrated guide will enable the insect enthusiast to identify most of the phasmids that are likely to be encountered in Peninsular Malaysia and Singapore. Only the latest valid phasmid names and details of food-plants where known

---

* Malayan refers to West Malaysia or Peninsular Malaysia only.

are given. All insects described are illustrated by line drawings of both sexes where possible. Insects are usually drawn from live or freshly dead specimens. Rarely encountered insects, which have not been caught by the author, may be illustrated by reference to a preserved specimen or by a redrawn sketch based on a published drawing. *Phobaeticus pinnipes* and *Parasipyloidea subtilis* are not illustrated in this book as both type as well as living specimens are not available. Text is kept to a minimum except for new species/the undescribed sex of a known species, where full descriptions are given.

This guide lists 111 West Malaysian and Singaporean phasmid species, not counting two subspecies and six unidentified species. One Javan species is included for clarity. Six new species are described together with two new genera, *Sceptrophasma* and *Lobonecroscia* and two species previously recorded only from Sumatra or Sarawak.

Only the valid name is given in this guide. A full listing of synonyms and location of type specimens as well as type localities may be found in Brock 1999 or are listed in this book if the species are newly described. This is followed by the body lengths of both sexes where these are known. Known foodplants of the species are then listed. For new species, full descriptions are given herein and will aid immediate identification of the insect. Where several species of a genus may be found in either Peninsular Malaysia or Singapore, a key is given to help in differentiating these insects. Full keys to all species are not, otherwise included in this catalogue, for the sake of brevity as the keys in Brock 1999 may be consulted when required.

ANAREOLATAE

FAMILY HETERONEMIIDAE
SUBFAMILY HETERONEMIINAE

Pseudobactricia ridleyi (Kirby 1904) (Plate 1)

Known only from the Holotype male from Singapore.
125 mm.
FOODPLANT: Unknown.

SUBFAMILY PACHYMORPHINAE

Sceptrophasma Brock & Seow-Choen gen. nov.

Small insects, males very slender, females more robust with long, slender legs. Head about 2 × longer than wide, eyes small. Antenna extremely short; 16–17 segments. First two segments very broadened, leaf-like, basal segment 2 × longer than second segment. Antenna slightly longer in male, but length of head and antenna not reaching 1/2 length of fore femur. Pronotum very shortened, about 1/2 length of head. Mesonotum elongate with some granulations, 5–7 × length of pronotum. Metanotum shorter than mesonotum. Abdomen long and slender. Female: operculum flat, rounded at tip, not reaching 1/2 length of anal segment. End of anal segment rounded. Male: subgenital plate swollen, truncate at apex; just exceeding end of 9th abdominal segment. End of anal segment slightly incised in centre. All legs long and slender, fore legs longest. All femora with pair of apical spines, otherwise legs smooth.

Related to *Gratidia* Stål (which also glues eggs onto suitable surfaces), *Sceptrophasma* is easily distinguished from it, by the more robust female, genitalia differences and shorter cerci compared with *Gratidia*. In addition, *Gratidia* species are primarily distributed in Africa and the Middle East and the few Asian species appear to be wrongly placed.

TYPE SPECIES: *Bacillus hispidulus* Wood-Mason, 1873, here designated (p. 47, pl. 7.2 male, 7.3 female). Syntypes: 3 males, 3 females. India: South Andaman Islands (NZSI), male India, Arakan coast, coll. Dr Stoliczka (NZSI) (=*Sceptrophasma hispidula* (Wood-Mason) comb. nov.—here transferred from the genus *Paraclitumnus* Brunner). (Lectotype not designated, as it has not been possible to examine material believed to be lodged in NZSI. However, Wood-Mason's figures clearly match culture stocks ex. Andaman Islands.) Other species: *Sceptrophasma langkawicensis* Seow-Choen sp nov. (Langkawi Islands, Malaysia)

ETYMOLOGY: From the Latin 'Sceptrum', meaning sceptre, walking-stick, staff or wand.

Sceptrophasma langkawicensis Brock & Seow-Choen sp. nov. (Plate 2)

FEMALE: A small stick-like wingless insect of light brown to dark brown coloration with short antennae. There is a lighter stripe above the eye bilaterally and a darker stripe just behind the eye. Darker areas are found over the mesonotum, metanotum and the upper parts of the abdominal segments. The underside of the insect and all legs are mottled brown. Some specimens have apple green mid and hind legs. The first antennal segment is broadened and the entire antenna is less than one-fifth the length of the fore femur. The antenna has 16 segments, the first two are broadened; the last considerably longer than the other segments. The head is much longer than wide. All legs are smooth and unarmed. The pronotum is much shorter than the head. The mesothorax is over five times the length of the pronotum; the metanotum is shorter than the mesonotum and both segments are very finely granulated. End of anal segment is almost rounded, slightly incised in the centre. Cercus long and exceeds the length of the 10th abdominal segment. The operculum is flat and does not exceed the end of the anal segment.

MALE: A thin brown fragile-looking wingless insect. There is a thin black stripe running from the base of the mesonotum to the anal segment. The stripes on the head resembles those of the female. The first antennal segment is slightly broadened and the antenna is much shorter than the fore femur. The antennal segments appear indistinct in the paratype. The anal segment is incised in the centre. The cerci are long and crossed. All legs are smooth and unarmed.

EGGS: The long light brown eggs are glued singly to twigs and branches. Eggs measure about 0.9 × 0.1 × 0.1 cm.

HOLOTYPE: Female, West Malaysia, Pulau Langkawi, Seven Wells, 25.XI.1995. F. Seow-Choen, I. Seow-En & C.S. Siow (in the collection of The Zoological Reference Collection, National University of Singapore).

PARATYPES: Male, West Malaysia, Pulau Langkawi, Seven Wells, 25.XI.95. F. Seow-Choen, I. Seow-En & C.S. Siow (in the collection of F. Seow-Choen). Female, West Malaysia, Pulau Langkawi, Seven Wells, 25.XI.95. F. Seow-Choen, I. Seow-En & C.S. Siow (one in collection of F. Seow-Choen, two in the collection of Pusat Sistematik Serangga, UKM Bangi, two in the collection of FRIM, Kepong, one in the collection of F. Seow-Choen).

MEASUREMENTS IN MM

		Holotype	Male Paratype	Female Paratype
Total body length		59	42	61–72
Antennae		4	5.5	5–6
Head		3	2.5	4
Pronotum		2.5	1.5	2.5
Mesonotum		13	10	14–17.5
Metanotum		7.5	6.5	8–10
Median segment		2	1	2
Fore-legs:	femur	22	18.5	21–25
	tibia	22	20	22–25

	tarsus	6.5	6.5	6–9
Mid-legs:	femur	16	12	15–19
	tibia	14.5	13	15–19
	tarsus	5	4.5	4–6
Hind-legs:	femur	20	15.5	19–22
	tibia	21.5	19	20–24
	tarsus	6	6	4.5–7

FOODPLANT: *Rubus moluccanus, Clidemia hirta, Melastoma malabathricum.*

ETYMOLOGY: Named after Pulau Langkawi the type locality. The insect has since been found in Tapah in some abundance by the author.

SUBFAMILY LONCHODINAE

Key to females of *Caurausius*

1. Head, no spines or double spined but not crested; fore legs broadened 3
   Head with/without a two-horned crest 2

2. Lowland species, front first tarsus prominently lobed,egg with a prominent hook like
      shape at one end .... *Carausius nodosus*
   Highland species, front first tarsus not prominently lobed, egg rounded ....
   .... *Carausius tanahrataensis*

3. Abdominal segment 7 broadened laterally .... *Carausius spinosus*
   Abdominal segments not lobed laterally 4

4. Fore first tarsus lobed .... *Carausius crawangenesis*
   Front tarsus not prominently lobed .... *Carausius globosus*

Key to males of *Carausius*

1. Thorax with a pair of nodules at apex of metathorax 2
   Thorax without a pair of nodules at apex of metathorax 3

2. Lowland species, thorax with tubercles, front first tarsus prominently lobed ....
   .... *Carausius nodosus*
   Highland species, thorax smooth, front first tarsus not prominently lobed ....
   .... *Carausius tanarataensis*

3. Anal segment C-arch shaped .... *Carausius spinosus*
   Anal segment not C arched shaped 4

4.   Anal segment bulb shaped .... *Carausius globosus*
     Anal segment split in centre; normal .... *Carausius crawangensis*

Carausius crawangensis (de Haan 1842) (Plate 3)

FEMALE: 121–122 mm.

MALE: Here described for the first time after a mating pair was found at 18 km Tapah Hills, Perak.

The male is a plain looking insect of light brown coloration. Each femur bears three minute subapical spines. The head bears two small spines. The mesothorax is only very faintly granular. Only the front first tarsus bears a large lobe as in the female. The eggs are unusual for eggs of *Carausius* species as they are not rounded.

MEASUREMENTS OF THE MALE N MM

Total body length		99
Antennae		56
Head		2.5
Pronotum		3
Mesonotum		25
Metanotum		15.5
Median segment		3.5
Fore-legs:	femur	21
	tibia	22
	tarsus	6
Mid-legs :	femur	19
	tibia	19
	tarsus	5
Hind-legs:	femur	22
	tibia	26
	tarsus	6

FOODPLANT: *Mangifera indica* and *Rubus moluccanus*.

Carausius nodosus (de Haan 1842) (Plate 4)

Two separate species were described inadvertently by Brock 1999 as *Carausius nodosus*. The first species is the lowland species from Singapore. This species fits exactly the male lectotype as designated by Brock 1995 and the male as illustrated by de Haan 1842, p. 133, pl. 11:3. The female illustrated by de Haan was that of *Lonchodes brevipes*. The female is therefore redescribed herein. The species from Tanah Rata in the Cameron Highlands is a separate species.

MALE: 89–105 mm.

DESCRIPTION OF THE FEMALE: The female is a long stick-like insect with a pair of raised horn-like structure on its head. Coarse granulations are present over the head, all thoracic segments as well as the abdomen. The anterior border of the mid-femur is reddish as in all species of *Carausius* in West Malaysia. Two subapical spines are present in all femora. The first tarsus of the front leg bears a lobe which is absent in the first tarsi of the hind and mid legs. The front tibia is broad and bears a wavy lobe about a third of the way down. The egg of *Carausius nodosus* is dark brown with black markings and measures 3 × 2 × 2 mm. There is a prominent hook-like structure at the far pole away from the capitulum.

MEASUREMENTS OF THE FEMALE IN MM

Total body length		125–134
Antennae		50–55
Head		4
Pronotum		4
Mesonotum		31–32
Metanotum		18
Median segment		8.5
Fore-legs:	femur	27–28
	tibia	25–26
	tarsus	7
Mid-legs :	femur	22–24
	tibia	20–22
	tarsus	6
Hind-legs:	femur	26–27
	tibia	29–31
	tarsus	7

FOODPLANT: *Combretum paniculatum, Grewia acuminata, Rourea mimosoides, Rubus fruticosus, and R. moluccanus.*

Carausius tanahrataensis Seow-Choen sp. nov. (Plate 5)

FEMALE: A medium-sized insect generally dark brown or light brown. Fine granularity over the head, pronotum, mesonotum and metanotum as well as the abdomen. Underside of head, prosternum and mesosternum much lighter than the rest of the insect. Head possesses a raised ridge with more prominent tips bilaterally. The antenna is long and exceeds the length of the front femur but is shorter than the front leg. Front femur, front tibia and first front tarsus expanded, the hind and mid legs being more stick-like. All femora possess two subapical spines. The operculum slightly exceeds the 10th abdominal segment and is keel-like. The cerci is very short and barely visible.

MALE: A very thin stick-like species generally light brown. Mesosternum much lighter in colour than the rest of the insect. Head possesses two sharp spines. The rest of the insect is smooth except for two two lateral knobs just before the junction of the metanotum with the median segment. The antenna is long and exceeds the front femur but not the front leg. The front femur and tibia is slightly expanded but the hind and mid legs are thin and stick-like. The front first tarsus is slightly lobed.

EGGS: The eggs are oval in shape and bluish. The micropylar plate is circular.

HOLOTYPE: Female, West Malaysia, Cameron Highlands, Track 4, 17.VI.93. F. Seow-Choen, I. Seow-En.(in the collection of Zoological Reference Collection, National University of Singapore)

PARATYPES: 2 females. West Malaysia, Cameron Highlands, Track 4, 9.V.96. F. Seow-Choen & C.H. Diong (one in the collection of Pusat Sistematik Serangga, UKM Bangi, one in the collection of F. Seow-Choen). 2 males. West Malaysia, Cameron Highlands, Track 4, 9.V.96. F. Seow-Choen & C.H. Diong (one in the collection of Pusat Sistematik Serangga, UKM Bangi, one in the collection of F. Seow-Choen). 1 male. West Malaysia, Cameron Highlands, Track 4, 10.V.96. F. Seow-Choen & C.H. Diong (in the collection of F. Seow-Choen).

MEASUREMENTS IN MM

		Holotype	Female Paratype	Male Paratype
Total body length		122	112–116	80–84
Antennae		33	38–40	44
Head		4	4	3
Pronotum		4	4	3
Mesonotum		29	25	20–22
Metanotum		15	14	11
Median segment		6	6	4
Fore-legs:	femur	23	23	20–22
	tibia	23	21	21–22
	tarsus	6	6	5–6
Mid-legs :	femur	19	18–19	15–16
	tibia	22	22	15–16
	tarsus	6	6	5–6
Hind-legs:	femur	20	20	18–19
	tibia	19	19–22	20–22
	tarsus	6	6	6

FOODPLANT: This species was found in Track 4, Tanah Rata. In captivity, the species took *Rubus moluccanus*.

ETYMOLOGY: This species is named after Tanah Rata, Cameron Highlands, the type locality and the only place where this species has been found so far.

Carausius globosus Brunner von Wattenwyl 1907 (Plate 6)

FEMALE: 147–165 mm. MALE: 90–110 mm.
FOODPLANT: *Grewia acuminata, Mangifera indica, Psidium guajava* and *Rubus moluccanus.*

Carausius spinosus Brunner von Wattenwyl 1907 (Plate 7)

FEMALE: 139–159 mm. MALE: 85–92 mm.
FOODPLANT: *Grewia acuminata, Ligustrum simense, Mangifera indica* and *Rubus moluccanus.*

Key to females of *Lonchodes*

1. Large opercular spine present; front first tarsus lobed; abdomen never with warts or spines .... *Lonchodes brevipes*
    Opercular spine absent, front first tarsus not lobed, abdomen often with warts or spines .... *Lonchodes geniculatus*

Key to males of *Lonchodes*

1. Head double spined; head, thorax and abdomen minute tubercles 2
    Head unarmed, thorax and abdomen smooth; end of abdomen with large expansion ...
    .... *Lonchodes skapanus*

2. Reddish brown; front first tarsus lobed .... *Lonchodes brevipes*
    Greenish with orange femoral apices, front first tasus not strongly lobed ....
    .... *Lonchodes geniculatus*

Lonchodes brevipes Gray 1835 (Plate 8 & 9)

Males and females from Singapore, including Pulau Ubin are smaller than specimens from West Malaysia. The latter specimens also possess slightly enlarged 5th and 6th abdominal segments unlike the Singapore specimens. Males from Singapore also possess less arched metathoraces.
West Malaysian
FEMALE: 146–157 mm. MALE: 89–107 mm.
Singaporean
FEMALE: 111–117 mm. MALE: 72–85 mm.
FOODPLANT: *Acacia auriculiformis, Combretum paniculatum,* Garden rose, *Grewia acuminata, Hibiscus rosa-sinensis, Psidium guajava, Rubus fruticosus, R. moluccanus, Uncaria gambir* and *Uncaria* spp.

Lonchodes geniculatus Gray 1835 (Plate 10)

FEMALE: 97–130 mm. MALE: 92–106 mm.

FOODPLANT: *Aidia wallichiana, Combretum paniculatum, Ficus fistulosa, Ilex macrophylla, Psychotria cf rostrata, Rubus moluccanus, R. fruticosus,.Uncaria cordata, U. gambir* and *Urophyllum glabrum.*

NOTES: The male is apple green with orangey femoral apices. The female displays a wide range of coloration from light brown to black blotches and stripes. There is a variety of warts and granulations over the thoraces and abdominal segments of the female; the commonest being lumps over the second abdominal and sixth abdominal segments and a spine at the end of the 5th abdominal segment.

Lonchodes skapanus Brock 1999 (Plate 11)

MALE: 118 mm, only sex known.
FOODPLANT: Unknown.

Menexenus unnoi Brock 1999 (Plate 12)

This species displays a wide range of colours in the wild, ranging from dark brown to bright green and even white. Some specimens show stripes or piebald coloration. The specimens from Fraser's Hill are larger than those from Tanah Rata.
Tanah Rata:
FEMALES: 43–53 mm. MALES: 37–43 mm.
Fraser's Hill:
FEMALES: 60–63 mm. MALES: 52–53 mm.

FOODPLANT: *Eucalyptus robusta, Grewia acuminata, Mangifera indica, Rubus moluccanus* and various low-lying ferns.

Key to *Prisomera*

1. Abdominal segments with paired or triplicated spines, head double spined 2
    Abdominal segments without spines, head with raised tubercles only in females, double spined in males .... *Prisomera malaya*

2. Head spines pointing backwards; paired spines on abdomen; end of abdominal segment truncate in females .... *Prisomera repudiosa*
    Head spines never pointing backwards; triplicated spines on abdomen; anal segment tapered in females .... *Prisomera verruculosa*

Prisomera malaya (Stål 1875) (Plate 13)

FEMALE: 98–104 mm. MALE: 81–89 mm.

FOODPLANT: *Aidia allichiana, Antidesma cuspidatum, Grewia acuminata, Psidium guajava, Rubus fruticosus, R. moluccanus, Timonius wallichianum, Uncaria gambir, Urophyllum glabrum* and various low-lying ferns.

Prisomera verruculosa (Brunner von Wattenwyl 1907) (Plate 14 & 15)

The mesonotal spines in female specimens from Tapah Hills are more prominent and sharper than those from Tanah Rata and the former specimens are also larger in size.
Tanah rata:

FEMALE: 62–67 mm. MALE: 42–45.

Tapah Hills:

FEMALE: 81–82 mm. MALE: 53–59.

FOODPLANT: *Mangifera indica, Rubus moluccanus* and various low growing ferns.

Prisomera repudiosa (Brunner von Wattenwyl 1907) (Plate 16)

FEMALE: 70–82 mm. MALE: 57–64 mm.

FOODPLANT: *Mangifera indica, Psidium guajava, Rubus moluccanus* and various low growing ferns.

SUBFAMILY NECROSCIINAE

Acacus sarawacus (Westwood 1859) (Plate 17)

FEMALE: 88–91 mm. MALE: 72–75 mm.

This species has not been found in West Malaysia but is found commonly in East Malaysia. There are two forms there. The lowland form is similar in size to the Singapore specimens, whereas the form from Mount Kinabalu is much smaller in size.

FOODPLANT: *Lithocarpus ewyckii, Psidium guajava, Pyracantha* sp., *Rosa* sp., *Rubus moluccanus* and *R. fruticosus*.

Anarchodes magnificus Brock 1999 (Plate 18)

FEMALE: 77–84 mm. MALE: 57–61 mm.

FOODPLANT: Unknown.

Key to *Asceles*

1. Mesothorax double spined .... *Asceles brevicollis*
   Mesothorax with many tubercles but no spines 2

2. End of fore tibia and front first tarsus broadened .... *Asceles validus*
   End of fore tibia not broadened 3

3. Abdominal segments 7–9 lobed .... *Asceles larunda*
   Abdominal segments 7–9 not lobed 4

4. Elongate species, egg very elongate .... *Asceles malaccae*
   "Compact" length, egg more globose 5

5. Lowland species; large with longest wings .... *Asceles tanarata singapura*
   Not found in the lowlands 6

6. Highland species; small with very short wings .... *Asceles tanarata tanarata*
   Mid-level species; medium-sized with longer wings .... *Asceles tanarata amplior*

Asceles malaccae (Saussure 1868) (Plate 19)

FEMALE: 95–97 mm. MALE: 74–84 mm.
FOODPLANT: *Bridelia tomentosa, Clidemia hirta, Elaeocarpus stipularis, Macaranga conifera, M. gigantea, M. triloba,* and *Microdesmis caseariifolia.*

Asceles brevicollis Redtenbacher 1908 (Plate 20)

FEMALE: 62–63 mm.
FOODPLANT: Unknown.

Asceles validus Redtenbacher 1908 (Plate 21)

FEMALE: 93–102 mm.
DESCRIPTION OF THE MALE: The male bears a resemblance to the female. It is generally brownish, with faint whitish stripes over the head, pronotum and 8th and 9th abdominal segments laterally. All the femora are strikingly broadened giving the insect a robust appearance. The 7th, 8th and 9th abdominal segments are slightly flared compared to the rest of the abdomen. The mid and hind tibiae and tarsi are thin and not expanded in anyway. The front tibia bears a slight flange as in the female. The front first tarsus is also slightly broadened. The mesonotum, mesosternum and metasternum are heavily

granulated. Both mesosternum and metasternum are orangey in colour. The hind wings are smokey brown.

MEASUREMENTS OF THE MALE IN MM

Total body length		77–80
Antennae		59–60
Head		3
Pronotum		3.5
Mesonotum		10.5–11
Metanotum		8–9
Median segment		3
Elytra		7
Hind-wings		48–49
Fore-legs:	femur	25
	tibia	24–27
	tarsus	10
Mid-legs :	femur	16
	tibia	14
	tarsus	6
Hind-legs:	femur	23
	tibia	20–21
	tarsus	8–9

The foodplant of the insect is unknown.

Asceles larunda (Westwood 1859) (Plate 22)

FEMALE: 65–75 mm. MALE: 45–47 mm.
FOODPLANT: *Macaranga conifera, M. gigantea* and *M. triloba.*

Asceles tanarata tanarata Brock 1999 (Plate 23)

Brock and Seow-Choen & Brock in Brock 1999 lists *Asceles tanarata tanarata* and *Asceles singapura* as new species and *Asceles tanarata amplior* as a new subspecies. I have carefully re-examined numerous examples of the three taxa and there are no specific differences between them indicating that they are full separate species. These specimens represent the zoogeographical clinal within a species. The largest insect with the longest wings are found in the lowlands; *Asceles singapura* has been found in Singapore, Mount Pulai and Tasek Chini. These localities are less than 1000 feet above sea level. The intermediate form, *Asceles tanarata amplior* may be found at Fraser's Hill and at Genting Highlands at about 3–4000 feet above sea level. The smallest form with the shortest wings *Asceles tanarata tanarata* has so far been found only at Tanarata between 5–6000 feet above sea level. All three forms are not sympatric. These should be treated as subspecies only. *Asceles tanarata tanarata* as the first species described in Brock 1999 has page priority and is here used as the specific name. *Asceles singapura* is renamed *Asceles tanarata singapura* subsp. comb. nov.

FEMALE: 37–44mm. MALE: 31–37 mm.

Wings of female not reaching end of 3rd abdominal segment. Wings of male to 2nd abdominal segment.

FOODPLANT: *Macaranga triloba.*

Asceles tanarata amplior Brock 1999 (Plate 24)

FEMALE: 46–59 mm. MALE: 45–48 mm.

Wings just exceed 4th abdominal segment in both sexes.

FOODPLANT: *Macaranga triloba.*

Asceles tanarata singapura Seow-Choen & Brock 1999 subsp. comb. nov. (Plate 25)

Asceles singapura Seow-Choen & Brock 1999, Brock 1999: 57–59.

FEMALE: 63–75. MALE: 54–60 mm.

Wings in female just exceeding the 5th abdominal segment and in the male the 7th abdominal segment.

FOODPLANT: *Macaranga conifera* and *M. gigantea, M. triloba.*

Asceles sp. 1 (unidentified) (Plate 26)

MALE: 60 mm

Found at Tapah Hills.

Asceles sp. 2 (unidentified) (Plate 27)

MALE: 74 mm

Found at Bangi, Selangor.

Asceles sp. 3 (unidentified) (Plate 28)

FEMALE: 75 mm

Found at Tapah Hills.

Baculofractum insignis (Brunner 1907) (Plate 29)

FEMALE: 138–156 mm. MALE: 109–130 mm.
FOODPLANT: *Croton argyratus* and *Rubus moluccanus.*

Key to *Calvisia*

1. Pre-anal part of hind wings not spotted 2
   Pre-anal part of hind wings spotted 4

2. Pre-anal part of hind wings mainly dark green 3
   Pre-anal part of hind wings a mixture of colours green with brownish and yellowish
       margins .... *Calvisia hemus*

3. Hind wings tesselated black and white, mesothorax double spined ..... *Calvisia virbius*
   Hind wings not tesselated uniform black, mesothorax not spined ....
       .... *Calvisia coerulescens*

4. Main colour of pre-anal part brown with blue/black spots .... *Calvisia sangarius*
   Main colour not a light brown, with spots 5

5. Main colour of pre-anal part green with blue/green spots in female;brownish with
       blue/black spots in male .... *Calvisia clarissima*
   Pre-anal part of hind wings coloured in blotches rather than spots on a background
       colour 6

6. Blotches of brown, buff, or black with black spots .... *Calvisia conicipennis*
   Pre-anal part of hind wings blotches of green/black and buff .... *Calvisia medora*

Calvisia hemus (Westwood 1859) (Plate 30)

FEMALE: 50 mm. MALE: 38–42 mm.
FOODPLANT: Unknown.

Calvisia sangarius (Westwood 1859) (Plate 31)

FEMALE: 61–64 mm. MALE: 45 mm.
FOODPLANT: *Scorodocarpus borneensis.*

Calvisia virbius (Westwood 1859) (Plate 32)

FEMALE: 55–64 mm. MALE: 45 mm.
FOODPLANT: *Mangifera indica*.

Calvisia conicipennis (Bates 1865) (Plate 33)

FEMALE: 71–74 mm. MALE: 54–56 mm.
FOODPLANT: *Euodia latifolia*.
Calvisia acute-gibbosus (Redtenbacher 1908) is very closely related to *Calvisia conicipennis*. The former hails from East Malaysia. My examination of specimens shows that there is only very slight difference between the two species and that they are probably best described as subspecies only. The chief difference being that *Calvisia acute-gibbosus* has the angle of the fore wings much sharper than that in *Calvisia conicipennis* in both male and female. *Calvisia acute-gibbosus* should therefore be renamed *Calvisia conicipennis acute-gibbosus* ssp. comb. nov.

Calvisia clarissima Redtenbacher 1908 (Plate 34)

FEMALE: 67–75 mm. MALE: 48–53 mm.
FOODPLANT: Unknown.

Calvisia coerulescens Redtenbacher 1908 (Plate 35)

FEMALE: 61–72 mm. MALE: Unknown.
FOODPLANT: Unknown.

Calvisia medora (Westwood 1859) (Plate 36)

This is a new record for Peninsular Malaysia. The only previous record of this species dates from the description by Westwood in 1859 and his specimens were from Sarawak. The male illustrated in this book was found by this author on a tree trunk on Mount Pulai in Johor in September 1992 during a daytime walk.
FEMALE: 69 mm. MALE: 40–49 mm.
Foodplant Unknown.

Centrophasma spinosum (Saussure 1868) (Plate 37)

FEMALE: 90–97 mm. MALE: 76–80 mm.
FOODPLANT: *Psidium guajava* and *Rubus moluccanus*.

Diacanthoidea diacanthos (de Haan 1842) (Plate 38)

FEMALE: 66–82 mm. MALE: 56–69 mm.
FOODPLANT: Unknown.

Key to *Diardia*

Slenderer insect, mesothorax tuberculated and spiny to an extent; wings long; front first
    tarsus lobed .... *Diardia diardi*
A thicker insect, mesothorax with numerous tubercles but no spines; wings reduced in
    length; tarsus not lobed .... *Diardi palliata*

Diardia diardi (de Haan 1842) (Plate 39 & 40)

Males of Bornean specimens may be up to 121 mm long. Females and some males
show a marked leaf-like lobe on the front first tarsal segment which is larger than the one
in West Malaysian specimens. The front femur and tibia of Bornean females are much
broader and expanded than West Malaysian specimens.
FEMALE: 124–138 mm. MALE: 84–113 mm.
FOODPLANT: Unknown.

Diardia palliata Redtenbacher 1908 (Plate 41)

FEMALE: 114–120 mm. MALE: Unknown.
FOODPLANT: Unknown.

Diesbachia tamyris (Westwood 1859) (Plate 42)

FEMALE: 108–128 mm. MALE: 89–96 mm.
FOODPLANT: *Annona muricata, Nothaphoebe umbelliflora, Psidium guajava, Rubus
fruticosus, R. moluccanus* and *Urophyllum glabrum.*

Key to *Gargantuoidea*

1. Mesothorax with 8–10 lateral spines 2
    Mesothorax with 17–20 lateral spines; hind wings brown ....
    .... *Gargantuoidea triumphalis*

2. Hind wings tesselated dark brown and white with a whitish border near the apex ....
    .... *Gargantuoidea tessellata*
    Hind wings pale brown with a buff spot near apex .... *Gargantuoidea phaetusa*

Gargantuoidea phaetusa (Westwood 1859) (Plate 43)

FEMALE: 120–121 mm. MALE: 96 mm.
FOODPLANT: Unknown.

Gargantuoidea triumphalis Redtenbacher 1908 (Plate 44)

FEMALE: 134–138 mm. MALE: 96–98 mm.
FOODPLANT: Unknown.

Gargantuoidea tessellata Redtenbacher 1908 (Plate 45)

FEMALE: 118–128 mm. MALE: 83 mm.
FOODPLANT: Unknown.

Key to *Lopaphus*

1. Fore wings/hind wings never present 4
   Fore wings/hind wings may be present 2

2. Normal fore wings; long hind wings; mouthparts red .... *Lopaphus brachypterus*
   Normal fore wings and hind wings never present in females 3

3. Normal fore wings may be present in males; fore wings absent, or truncated cone shaped or rounded in females; hind wings may be absent, short or long in male; females never with hind wings; mouthparts red .... *Lopaphus iolas*
   Very small hind wings present in both sexes; very small fore wings ....
   .... *Lopaphus nanoalatus*

4. Prominent subapical spine on femora;mouthparts red .... *Lopaphus perakensis*
   Subtle presence of subapical spine on femora; mouthparts light brown ....
   .... *Lopaphus suwinae*

Lopaphus brachypterus (de Haan 1842) (Plate 46)

FEMALE: 83–113 mm. MALE: 55–62 mm.
FOODPLANT: *Aidia wallichiana* and *Psidium guajava*.

Lopaphus iolas (Westwood 1859) (Plate 47–49)

FEMALE: 82–116 mm. MALE: 64–80 mm.
FOODPLANT: *Cinnamomum iners, Piper aduncum, Psidium guajava, Rubus moluccanus.*

This insect is perhaps the commonest and most widespread of phasmids in West Malaysia. Indeed members of the genus range from India to Australia. Brock(1998) lists *Lopaphus iolas*(Westwood) and *Lopaphus langkawicus* (Brock) as separate species mainly because of the presence of wings in *Lopaphus iolas* and the absence of wings in *Lopaphus langkawicus*. Nonetheless, an examination of insects collected from all over West Malaysia shows the complete variation within this species and proves that *Lopaphus iolas* and *Lopaphus langkawicus* are one species. Within the species complex there a range of geographical variation from totally wingless males to males with very long wings. Females show a similar variation from one locality to the next; with some females being totally wingless and others having obvious rounded forewings. Hindwings are always lacking in females of this species. Besides the presence and the length of wings, insects from the various regions are otherwise totally indistinguishable.

Females from Kedah Peak measure from 103 to 118 mm. All specimens examined are entirely wingless. Very few tubercles are present on the head. Males from Kedah Peak measure 68–78 mm in body length. Wings are not present in these males.

Females from Langkawi Island measure 98–111 mm in body length. Wings are totally absent. Tubercles were not seen on the head. Males measure 72–78 mm and are also wingless. There are no discernable difference between these insects and those from Kedah Peak.

Females from Kepong, Genting Highlands, Ulu Gombak measure 94–111 mm in Body length. The fore wings are truncated, cone shaped and stick outwards away from the metanotum. Males measure 68–76 mm in body length and have hind wings not exceeding the third abdominal segment.

Specimens from Tasek Chini, Mount Pulai in Johore and Singapore are similar. Boby lengths of females vary from 101–119 mm and the fore wings although truncated are nicely rounded and closely applied to the metanotum. Tubercles may or may not be present on the head. Males from these regions measure 74–84 mm in body length. Hind wings in males just exceed the fifth abdominal segment.

In Tapah Hills, males of the wingless form and males with wings reaching to the fourth abdominal segments may be found.

There is therefore a gradual geographical variation. Furthermore, eggs from these forms are all similar.

Lopaphus perakensis (Redtenbacher 1908) (Plate 50)

FEMALE: 84–110 mm. MALE: 74–77 mm.
FOODPLANT: *Psidium guajava* and *Rubus moluccanus*.

Lopaphus nanoalatus Brock 1999 (Plate 51)

FEMALE: 64–70 mm. MALE: 48 mm.
FOODPLANT: *Rubus moluccanus*.

Lopaphus suwinae sp. nov. (Plate 52)

MALE: A very thin and fragile looking insect. Antennae exceeds the length of the fore femora. Generally brown in colour. No granulations or tubercles present on the mesothorax or metathorax or prothorax. The bases of all femora are apple green. The apices of all tibia are a dirty cream colour. Cream coloured bands are present on both sides of the prothorax, on the mesothorax just above the mid-legs, and on the metathorax just above the hind leg. There is also a white band on the side of the 9th and 10th abdominal segment. The cerci is visible above the 10th abdominal segment.

FEMALE: A short to medium length wingless stick-like insect. Antennae long and exceeds the length of the fore femora. Mouth parts not noticeably red unlike the other species of the genus in West Malaysia. Mid and hind legs greenish. Front leg is also green but with more brownish patches. The body and head are brown. Prothorax and mesothorax with numerous small tubercles. The head is generally smooth. Very small subapical spines are present on all femora. Wings are not present.

HOLOTYPE MALE: West Malaysia, Genting Highlands, near Awana 22.VI.96. F. Seow-Choen & Dolly Seow (in The Zoological Reference Collection, National University of Singapore).

PARATYPES: Two Females. West Malaysia, Genting Highlands, near Awana 7.12.96. F. Seow-Choen & I. Seow-En (one in The Zoological Reference Collection, National University of Singapore and one in collection F. Seow-Choen).

MEASUREMENTS IN MM

	Holotype Male	Female Paratypes
Total body length	57.5	73–88
Antennae	65	51–55
Head	2	3–4
Pronotum	2	3–3
Mesonotum	15	18–19
Metanotum	4	3.5–4
Median segment	3	3.5–4
Fore-legs: femur	20	18.5–20.5
tibia	21	19.5–22.5
tarsus	9.8	9–10
Mid-legs: femur	20.5	13.5
tibia	19.8	12.5
tarsus	6.5	7
Hind-legs: femur	21.5	20–22.5
tibia	25	17–19.5
tarsus	9.5	8.5–10

FOODPLANT: Unknown.

ETYMOLOGY: This species is named after Ms Lee Su Win of Tapah, who has been a pillar for the conservation movement in Malaysia. She has also been very helpful in ferrying the author to various places in search of phasmids as well as hosting the author in her beautiful forest home as a base for forest research in phasmids.

Lopaphus sp. (unidentified) (Plate 53)

FEMALE: 52 mm
Found at Tanah Rata.

Loxopsis seowi Brock 1999 (Plate 54)

FEMALE: 68–75 mm. MALE: 56 mm.
FOODPLANT: *Nephilium lappaceum.*
A closely related species *Loxopsis agondas* (Westwood 1859) occurs in Sarawak and has been found by the author in Gunung Mulu National Park.

Key to *Marmessoidea*

Thorax light green in female; dark green in male with blue head; both with a yellow spot on the head; hind wings bright pink; eggs glued to twigs .... *Marmessoidea rosea*
Thorax brown; hind wings brown; eggs pierced into leaves .... *Marmessoidea annulata*

Marmessoidea rosea (Fabricius 1793) (Plate 55)

FEMALE: 68–82 mm. MALE: 45–57 mm.
FOODPLANT: *Cinnamomum iners.*

Marmessoidea annulata (Fabricius 1798) (Plate 56)

FEMALE: 86–91 mm. MALE: 60–62 mm.
FOODPLANT: *Annona muricata, Enicosanthum membranifolium, Oxymitra glauca* and *Psychotria viridiflora.*

Key to *Necroscia*

1. Hind wings rosy 2
    Hind wings colourless 5

2.   Thorax and pre-anal part of hind wing light green without spots/markings ....
      .... *Necroscia kotatinggia*
      Thorax and pre-anal part of hind wings not light green 3

3.   Thorax and pre-anal part of hind wings dark green without other markings ....
      .... *Necroscia inflata*
      Thorax and pre-anal part of hind wings with other markings 4

4.   Fore-wings and pre-anal part of hind wings dark green; bordered with a red and white
      line .... *Necroscia marginata*
      Fore wings and pre-anal part of hind wings with a prominent white line ....
      .... *Necroscia prasina*

5.   Fore wings green with a blackish mauve area and a yellow spot .. *Necroscia annulipes*
      Fore wings and Pre-anal part of hind wings variously coloured and spotted 6

6.   Slenderer species, brownish orange with yellow spots; thorax smooth ....
      .... *Necroscia westwoodi*
      Larger species; thorax tuberculated 7

7.   Medium-sized species; small tubercles especially prominent on either side of the
      median, various colours including green, red, yellow black; all with yellow spots ....
      .... *Necroscia punctata*
      Larger species; small tubercles on thorax well spread out; various colours including
      green, yellow, brown .... *Necroscia affinis*

Necroscia marginata (Gray 1835) (Plate 57)

FEMALE: 60–64 mm. MALE: 40–44 mm.
FOODPLANT: *Uncaria cordata* and *U. gambir.*

Necroscia punctata (Gray 1835) (Plate 58)

FEMALE: 68–85 mm. MALE: 52–63 mm.
FOODPLANT: *Cinnamomum iners.*

Necroscia affinis (Gray 1835) (Plate 59)

FEMALE: 80–90 mm. MALE: 63–67 mm.
FOODPLANTS: *Anisophylla disticha, Cinnamomum iners, Eurya acuminata, Melastoma sanguineum, Neonauclea excelsa* and *Olea brachiata.*

Necroscia annulipes (Gray 1835) (Plate 60)

FEMALE: 76–93 mm. MALE: 62–63 mm.
FOODPLANT: *Olea brachiata.*

Necroscia prasina (Burmeister 1838) (Plate 61)

FEMALE: 65–73 mm. MALE: 48–55 mm.
FOODPLANT: *Cinnamomum iners* and *Gomphandra quadrifida.*

Necroscia westwoodi Kirby 1904 (Plate 62)

FEMALE: 62–68 mm. MALE: 47–54 mm.
FOODPLANT: *Psychotria malayana.*

Necroscia inflata (Redtenbacher 1908) (Plate 63)

FEMALE: 65–78 mm. MALE: 53–59 mm.
FOODPLANTS: *Adina rubescens, Aidia wallichiana, Beilschmioda palembanica, Mussaenda glabra, Pertusadina eurhyncha, Uncaria cordata* and *U. gambir.*

Necroscia kotatinggia Brock 1999 (Plate 64)

MALE: 58–62 mm.
A male of this species was found by the author at Mount Serapi in Sarawak.

FEMALE: A winged stick insect which is generally light green. The eyes are a dark brown colour. Three ocelli are present on the head. The mesonotum is very finely granulated.The hind wings are a bright pink colour. The cerci are noticeably large. The operculum is keel-shaped and exceeds the 10th abdominal segment.

MEASUREMENTS OF THE FEMALE IN MM

Total body length	84–85
Antennae	61–64
Head	3.5
Pronotum	3.5–4
Mesonotum	12
Metanotum	7
Median segment	4
Fore-legs: femur	22
tibia	20

	tarsus	11
Mid-legs :	femur	14–14.5
	tibia	10–10.5
	tarsus	6
Hind-legs:	femur	21
	tibia	18
	tarsus	8.5

Lobonecroscia Brock & Seow-Choen gen. nov.

Small, slender bodied insects, sexes rather different in appearance, male very fragile-looking, female more robust. Head 1.6 × longer than wide, eyes large. Antenna 1.5 to 2 × length of fore leg. Pronotum slightly shorter than head with several granulations. Mesonotum 3 to more than 4.5 × length of pronotum. Metanotum slightly shorter than mesonotum. Abdomen long and slender, slightly hairy, some segments lobed laterally in females only. Female: operculum long, rounded at tip; almost reaching end of anal segment. Male: subgenital plate small, pointed at tip, not quite reaching end of anal segment. Cercus moderate size, rounded at tip. Fore wing short, truncate. Hind wing large. Legs slender, moderately long; in female only fore femur with broad lobe, not quite reaching apex. Base of fore femur incurved.

The new species keys out near *Neoclides* Uvarov, which are much more robust species in both sexes, with lobed fore femora. In general appearance, *Lobonecroscia* resembles genera such as the delicate *Sosibia* Stål and *Necroscia* Serville.

TYPE SPECIES: *Lobonecroscia subflava* Brock & Seow-Choen sp. nov.

Lobonecroscia subflava Brock & Seow-Choen sp. nov. (Plate 65)

Unidentified species. Brock 1998: 166 figure of female.
Unidentified species. Seow-Choen 1997: 99 figure of female, 100 colour figures 80, 81 of male.

FEMALE HOLOTYPE: Attractive black, brown and whitish mottled insect with distinctly lobed fore femora. Head is dark brown, 1.6 × longer than wide with blackish outer patches from behind eye to back of head, large lighter brown/whitish brown patches between eyes. Eyes large, dark brown. Antenna almost 2 × length of fore femur, with narrow dark brown bands, conspicuous near base and towards tip. Pronotum slender, dark brown, longer than wide; shorter than head with several granultations. Mesothorax heavily granulated dorsally, laterally and ventrally (the latter with smaller granulations); segment almost 3 × length of pronotum, dark brown with large whitish and lighter brown patches. Ventral surface of mesothorax mainly dark brown except for three small, lighter brown patches, although end of segment light brown, extending to whole of metathorax. Metanotum slightly shorter (but same colour) than mesonotum. Abdomen long and slender, slightly hairy; dark brown with some whitish streaks/mottling. End of segments 4–7 lobed laterally, more conspicuous in segment 7. Segments 8–10 narrowed, segments shorter in length than previous segments. Anal segment slightly broadened laterally, tapering towards truncate tip. Operculum long, rounded at tip; almost reaching end of anal segment. Cercus broad, slightly tapered at tip, just visible beyond end of anal segment. Fore wings whitish brown, dark brown at margin; raised in centre, subtruncate. Pre-anal part of hind wings dark brown and whitish banded, in similar shades to mesonotum. Hind wings transparent, with brown veins. Legs generally yellowish with indistinct brown markings/bands except for fore femur, which is narrow, incurved at base, but broadened half way along its length, which forms a large lobe, not quite reaching apex. Lobe dark brown on upper part with whitish dots, whitish with brown dots beneath, ventral area dark brown. Basal area brownish, towards apex greenish. Mid-femur greenish yellow. Hind femur indistinctly banded with brown, continuing on tarsus. Tarsi with more brown areas than femora and tibiae.

FEMALE PARATYPE: Description as for Holotype except for colour differences. The insect is generally dark brown with yellow front tibiae, mid-legs and metasternum. The abdomen is dark brown with some paler discoloration over the upper aspects of the first 6 segments. The whitish spots on the head and mesothorax of the holotype are not present in the paratype and the upper aspect of the head and mesothorax of the paratype is generally dark brown. There are two faint darker lines running behind the eyes on both sides towards the back of the head. The posterior three quarters of the mesonotum is very slightly elevated with numerous fine granulations. This area is flanked bilaterally by a yellowish line. The lobed front femur is dark brown with bands, The hind leg is dark brown. The pre-anal part of the hind wings are brown with light patches.

MALE: Small, slender yellowish brown species with yellowish legs. Fore wings with yellow patch. Underside completely light yellowish brown. Head longer than wide, dark brown with large brown eyes; pale yellowish brown beneath eyes. Antenna as in female. Central black stripe starts after paler patch between eyes (similar to female). Pronotum shorter than head, upper part with dark brown blotch either side, with two further pairs of blotches on mesonotum. Two dark brown uneven lines run along the surface; of the granulated pronotum and mesonotum. Mesonotum over 4.5 × length of pronotum, with dark line conspicuous towards end of segment. Metanotum shorter. Abdomen long and slender, brown. End of anal segment rounded, slightly incised in centre. Cerci slender, rounded at tip, half length of anal segment. Fore wings short and truncate. Brown with bold yellow patch. Pre-anal part of hind wing brown with several whitish patches. Hind wing transparent with brown veins. All legs yellowish with small dark ring at apices of femora and tibiae.

FEMALE HOLOTYPE: Ulu Piah, Perak, February1985. M.K.P. Yeh; in copula with male. Natural History Museum, London)

FEMALE PARATYPE: Singapore. Bukit Timah Hill, VII.94. Francis Lim (in the collection of F. Seow-Choen).

MALE PARATYPES: Singapore, Island Country Club, XII.93, F. Seow-Choen & I. Seow-En (in the collection of F. Seow-Choen). Ulu Piah, Perak, II.1985, M.K.P. Yeh; in copula with female. Natural History Museum, London; Teluk Bahang Forest Recreation Park, Penang, P.D. Brock (in collection P.D. Brock).

MEASUREMENTS IN MM

		Female Holotype	Female paratypes	Male paratypes
Total body length		62	58	38–44
Antennae		42	34	34
Head		4	4	2.5–3
Pronotum		3	3	1.5–1.8
Mesonotum		8.5	9	7
Metanotum		4	4	3
Abdomen		–	31	27
Cercus		5	5	5
Wings:	fore	3	3	1–1.5
	hind	34	30	21
Fore-legs:	femur	10	10	9–10
	tibia	8	9	8–9
	tarsus	–	5.5	5.5
Mid-legs :	femur	6	6.5	7
	tibia	5.5	6	6
	tarsus	–	3.5	4
Hind-legs:	femur	9	10	9–10
	tibia	8.5	10	9
	tarsus	–	5	5

FOODPLANT: Unknown.

ETYMOLOGY: *Lobonecroscia* refers to the lobed fore femora present in females and its general affinity with the genus *Necroscia*. The specific epithet *subflava* refers to the partly yellowish appearance of both sexes, particularly the legs and fore-wings in the male.

Neoclides magistralis (Redtenbacher 1908) (Plate 66)

FEMALE: 76–77 mm. MALE: Unknown.
FOODPLANT: Unknown.

Orthonecroscia filum (Westwood 1848) (Plate 67)

FEMALE: 89–94 mm. MALE: 68–72 mm.
FOODPLANT: *Baccaurea montleyana* and *Melastoma sanguineum*.

Paranecroscia operculata Redtenbacher 1908 (Plate 68)

FEMALE: 42–56 mm. MALE: 32 mm.
FOODPLANT: Unknown.

Parasipyloidea subtilis Redtenbacher 1908

The type specimen in Vienna is in very poor condition (Brock, pers. comm.). I have not examined this type specimen, nonetheless, the description as given by Brock suggests a nymph of *Lopaphus iolas* and in my view the validity of this species is suspect.

FEMALE: 57 mm. MALE: Unknown.

FOODPLANT: Unknown.

Parasteneboea yehi Brock 1999 (Plate 69)

FEMALE: 50 mm. MALE: 36 mm.

FOODPLANT: Unknown.

DESCRIPTION OF THE MALE:

MALE: A very spiny small wingless insect which is generally brownish green. Darker bands are obvious over the legs. The head is longer than broad. The back of the head bears at least 10 spines gathered in a cluster. There is another pair anteriorly between the eyes. The antennae are also banded with darker and lighter areas. The back of the pronotum bears a pair of spines. Mesothorax very spiny; There is a pair of spine at the anterior edge of the mesothorax laterally. A large pair of spine projects laterally mid way down the mesothorax. In between the first pair and the mid mesothoracic pair of spine is a cluster of four spines; two pointing upwards and two pointing outwards. The base of the mesothorax bears 10 spines in a semicircumferential manner from the base of of coxa to the other side. The metathorax also bears 4 spines. There is a lateral spine just before the coxa of the hind leg. The base of the first 5 abdominal segments bears a spine like projection with the first 2 being less prominent. The lateral margin at the end of each segment is lobed. The end of the anal segment is incised at the centre and the cerci exceeds the length of the anal segment. All femora bears apical and subapical spines. All femora bears 3 large pairs of lobes and 1 to 2 smaller pairs nearer the base. All tibiae are unarmed. The first tarsus is very long.

MEASUREMENTS OF THE MALE IN MM

Total body length		36
Antennae		45
Head		3
Pronotum		2.5
Mesonotum		9
Metanotum		2
Median segment		2
Fore-legs:	femur	15
	tibia	14
	tarsus	10.5
Mid-legs :	femur	12
	tibia	11.5
	tarsus	7.5

Hind-legs:	femur	17
	tibia	16
	tarsus	11.5

Phaenopharos struthioneus (Westwood 1859) (Plate 70)

FEMALE: 145–182 mm. MALE: 108–130 mm.
FOODPLANT: *Psidium guajava, Rubus fruticosus* and *R. moluccanus.*

Scionecra microptera (Redtenbacher 1908) (Plate 71)

FEMALE: 69.5 mm. MALE: 49–50 mm.
FOODPLANT: Unknown.

Key to *Sipyloidea*

1. Hind wings pinkish 2
   Hind wings not pinkish 3

2. Thorax tuberculated; anal segment pointed; eggs glued to surfaces ....
   .... *Sipyloidea sipylus*
   Thorax not tuberculated; anal segment anal segment rounded with slight central
   indentation; eggs flicked at random .... *Sipyloidea perakensis*

3. Anal segment sharpely pointed; eggs glued to surfaces; hind wings brownish ....
   .... *Sipyloidea sordida*
   Anal segment not pointed at tip 4

4. Forewings and pre-anal part of hind wings brown in female; green and brown in
   males; hind wings brown in females; transparent in males ....
   .... *Sipyloidea meneptolemos*
   Forewings and pre-anal part of hind wings dark brown/black with stripes; hind wings
   brown .... *Sipyloidea magna*

Sipyloidea sordida (de Haan 1842) (Plate 72)

FEMALE: 53–56 mm. MALE: Unknown.
FOODPLANT: Unknown.

Sipyloidea sipylus (Westwood 1859) (Plate 73)

FEMALE: 82–89 mm. Male: 60 mm.

FOODPLANT: *Psidium guajava* and *Rubus moluccanus.*

DESCRIPTION OF THE MALE: The male is a very thin, fragile looking insect with antennae exceeding the length of the fore-legs. The insect is generally green with pinkish hind-wings. Several lighter bands are seen near the eyes on the lateral side of the head. There is a prominent whitish line on the side of the fore-wings. There are numerous very fine tubercles over the mesothorax. The cerci are crossed, but visible from the top of the insect.

MEASUREMENTS OF THE MALE IN MM

Total body length		60
Antennae		56
Head		2
Pronotum		2
Mesonotum		12
Metanotum		4
Median segment		3
Wings	Fore	4
	Hind	31
Fore-legs:	femur	19
	tibia	18.5
	tarsus	8
Mid-legs :	femur	8
	tibia	12
	tarsus	6
Hind-legs:	femur	17.5
	tibia	18
	tarsus	8

Sipyloidea meneptolemus (Westwood 1859) (Plate 74)

FEMALE: 79–90 mm. MALE: 51–57 mm.

FOODPLANT: *Psidium guajava.*

Sipyloidea magna Redtenbacher 1908 (Plate 75)

FEMALE: 90 mm. MALE: Unknown.

FOODPLANT: Unknown.

Sipyloidea perakensis Seow-Choen sp. nov. (Plate 76)

FEMALE: A generally brownish winged stick-insect. Fore femora slightly expanded, otherwise all legs are thin and stick-like. The occasional specimen shows several tubercles on the head, otherwise most insects have a smooth head. Mesothorax generally without tubercles or granulations. Tenth abdominal segment short and rounded with an incised indentation in the middle. The cerci are short and just visible beyond the 10th segment. The fore wings are distinctly elongated. The hind wings are light pink with the coastal part the same colour as the rest of the insect, which is a darker shade of brown.

MALE: A very thin winged green insect. There is a faint white line on the head just behind the eye. A very thin black line is seen on the side of the mesothorax. There is also a faint white-green line on the side of the fore wing and the coastal part of the hind wing. The hind wings are light pink. The cerci are visible above the end of the anal segment and are not crossed.

EGGS: The eggs were observed to be flicked randomly and not glued to surfaces.

HOLOTYPE: Female. West Malaysia, Ulu Piah, Perak, VIII.94. F. Seow-Choen & M. Yeh (in The Zoological Reference Collection, National University of Singapore)

PARATYPES: Two Females. West Malaysia, Ulu Piah, Perak, one 10.V.96, one 11.V.96, F. Seow-Choen & C.H. Diong (one in collection of Centre for Insect Systematics, Universiti Kebangsaan Malaysia, Bangi, and one in Collection F. Seow-Choen). Two Males. West Malaysia, Ulu Piah, Perak, VIII.94, F. Seow-Choen & M. Yeh (one in collection of Centre for Insect Systematics, Universiti Kebangsaan Malaysia, Bangi, and one in Collection F. Seow-Choen).

MEASUREMENTS IN MM

		Holotype	Female Paratypes	Male Paratypes
Total body length		89	88–89	57–62
Antennae		51	54–61	54–57
Head		3.5	3.5–4	2.5
Pronotum		3.5	3.5	2
Mesonotum		15	15	10
Metanotum		7	7	4
Median segment		4	4	2
Wings:	fore	8	7–8	4
	hind	58	52–54	28–29
Fore-legs:	femur	22	21–23	18–19
	tibia	20	22	18–19
	tarsus	10	9–10	8
Mid-legs :	femur	15	12–15	13
	tibia	13	8–12.5	11.5–12
	tarsus	7	7–9	5.5–6
Hind-legs:	femur	20	20	17.5–18
	tibia	20	19–21	18–18.5
	tarsus	8.5	8.5–9	7

FOODPLANT: *Psidium guajava* and *Rubus moluccanus*.
ETYMOLOGY: Named after the State of Perak, where Ulu Piah is situated.

Key to *Sosibia*

1. Head with spines 2
   Head without spines 4

2. Two of the head spines are spade like .... *Sosibia aurita*
   All head spines are pointed 3

3. Head spines orange/brown; prothorax, mesothorax spined .... *Sosibia curtipes*
   Head spines small; prothorax and front of mesothorax with tubercles or small spines .... *Sosibia nigrispina*

4. Front of mesothorax with spines; femora without subapical spine .... *Sosibia brocki*
   Mesothorax with granulations, tubercles not spines 5

5. Femora without subapical spines; smaller species .... *Sosibia esacus*
   Femora with subapical spines; larger species 6

6. Mesothorax 3–4 × length of prothorax; base of pre-anal part of hind wings normal .... *Sosibia solida*
   Mesothorax 5 × length of prothorax; base of pre-anal part of hind wings pink with a black blotch .... *Sosibia macera*

Sosibia aurita (Fabricius 1793) (Plate 77)

FEMALE: 63–90 mm. MALE: Unknown.
FOODPLANT: Unknown.

Sosibia curtipes (Westwood 1848) (Plate 78)

FEMALE: 100–121 mm. MALE: 76–80 mm.
FOODPLANT: Unknown.

Sosibia esacus (Westwood 1859) (Plate 79)

FEMALE: 66–75 mm. MALE: 41–58 mm.
FOODPLANT: *Ixonanthes reticulata* and *Salacia macrophylla*.

Sosibia nigrispina Stål 1875 (Plate 80)

FEMALE: 81–93 mm. MALE: 70–71 mm.
FOODPLANT: Unknown.

Sosibia solida Redtenbacher 1908 (Plate 81)

FEMALE: 99–114 mm. MALE: 70–78 mm.
FOODPLANT: Unknown.

Sosibia macera Redtenbacher 1908 (Plate 82)

FEMALE: 95–108 mm. MALE: 77 mm.
FOODPLANT: Unknown.

Sosibia brocki Seow-Choen sp. nov. (Plate 83)

FEMALE: A long thin winged-insect with short legs and long abdomen. Overall a greyish brown colour. The antennae is longer than the fore legs. The hind legs just reach the end of the hind wings which is slightly more than half way down the abdomen at the 5th abodominal segment. All femora lack subapical spines. The front femora are very short and greatly expanded. The mid and hind femora are thin and stick-like. The head and prothorax are not spined, but the meosothorax bears much granulations becoming a series of short spines anteriorly. The operculum is boat shaped and the end of the abdominal segment is slightly jutting with the cerci just visible from above. The fore wings are tear shaped and greenish grey as is the coastal part of the hind wings.

MALE: The male is a very thin winged insect. Ocelli are present on the head. The head and mesothorax are not spined but the mesothorax has numerous granulations becoming a series of short spines near the front next to the prothorax. All legs are long and only the front femora is very slightly expanded, but not to the extent of the female. The antennae is much longer than the fore legs. None of the femora bear subapical spines. The hind legs reach to the 7th or 8th abdominal segment and exceeds the hind wings which reaches the end of the 5th abdominal segment. The end of the fore wing is fringed by a faint greenish white line. The anal segment is rounded and triangularly incised in the centre. The cerci are not visible from above.

HOLOTYPE: Female. West Malaysia, Gunung Pulai, Johor, 8.XI.96. F. Seow-Choen, I Abercrombie & William Fleming (in the collection of F. Seow-Choen).

PARATYPES: Male. West Malaysia, Gunung Pulai, Johor, 8.XI.96, F. Seow-Choen, I Abercrombie & William Fleming (in the collection of F. Seow-Choen). Male. West Malaysia, Gunung Pulai, Johor, 8.XI.96, F. Seow-Choen, I Abercrombie & William Fleming (in The Zoological Reference Collection, National University of Singapore).

MEASUREMENTS IN MM

	Holotype	Male Paratypes
Total body length	112	68–72
Antennae	44	48–50
Head	3.5	2–2.5
Pronotum	3.5	2–2.5
Mesonotum	18.5	12.5–13.5
Metanotum	10	5
Median segment	4	2–2.5
Wings: fore	4.5	2–2.5
hind	54	32–31.5
Fore-legs: femur	12	13–14
tibia	10	11–12
tarsus	9	9
Mid-legs: femur	13	9.5–11
tibia	9	8
tarsus	6	5–6
Hind-legs: femur	19	12–15
tibia	12	16–17
tarsus	7	6–7

FOODPLANT: Unknown.

ETYMOLOGY: This insect is named after Mr Paul Brock who has studied West Malaysian phasmids extensively and clarified many of the issues in West Malaysian phasmid taxonomy.

Key to *Tagesoidea*

Smooth mesothorax; hind wings black with several white spots .... *Tagesoidea tages*
Thorax granulated with lateral spines; hind wings yellow with a black patterned band ....
.... *Tagesoidea nigrofasciata*

Tagesoidea tages (Westwood 1859) (Plate 84)

FEMALE: 46–52 mm. MALE: 39 mm.
FOODPLANT: Unknown.

Tagesoidea nigrofasciata Redtenbacher 1908 (Plate 85)

FEMALE: 77–90 mm. MALE: 55–58 mm.
FOODPLANT: Unknown.

Key to *Trachythorax*

Prothorax light brown with black stripes; mesothorax without a black V-shaped area ....
.... *Trachythorax atrosignatus*
Prothorax dark brown; mesothorax with a black V-shaped area .... *Trachythorax gohi*

Trachythorax atrosignatus (Brunner 1893) (Plate 86)

FEMALE: 66–74 mm. MALE: 39–43 mm.
FOODPLANT: Unknown.

Trachythorax gohi Brock 1999 (Plate 87)

FEMALE: 88 mm. MALE: Unknown.
FOODPLANT: Unknown.

FAMILY PHASMATIDAE
SUBFAMILY PHASMATINAE

Baculum nematodes (de Haan 1842) (Plate 88)

Specimens from Sarawak are the longest. Those from Tasek Chini, Singapore, Melaka, Selangor are intermediate in size. Specimens from Tapah Hills are the smallest. There is otherwise no discernible difference between these specimens nor in their eggs.
MT SERAPI, MT MULU: Sarawak Female: 199–211 mm. Male: 127–132 mm.
SINGAPORE, WEST MALAYSIA (except Tapah Hills): Female: 151–181 mm. Male: 103–133 mm.
TAPAH HILLS: Female; 116–127, Male: 85–96.
FOODPLANT: *Ampelociccus gracilis, Gomphandra quadrifida, Grewia acuminata, Imperata cylindrica, Leptonychia glabra, Mangifera indica, Microdesmis caseariifolia, Piper aduncum* and *Rubus moluccanus. Macaranga conifera* is not a foodplant but was previously misidentified.

Erringtonia malaccensis Brunner 1907 (Plate 89)

FEMALE: 150 mm. MALE: Unknown.
FOODPLANT: Unknown.

Parabaculum pendleburyi Brock 1999 (Plate 90)

FEMALE: 78–89 mm. MALE: 64 mm.
FOODPLANT: Unknown.

Eurycnema versirubra (Audinet-Serville 1838) (Plate 91)

FEMALE: 160–215 mm. MALE: 112–133 mm.
FOODPLANT: *Acacia auriculiformis*, *Eucalyptus robusta*, *Mangifera indica* and *Psidium guajava*.

Nearchus grubaueri Redtenbacher 1908 (Plate 92)

FEMALE: 209 mm. MALE: Unknown.
FOODPLANT: Unknown.

Key to *Pharnacia*

1. Head bituberculated 2
   Head smooth, legs spiny but not foliaceous; mesosternum and metasternum with purple spots; black band behind eye in males; pre-anal part of the hind wings in males are green with a white band laterally............................ *Pharnacia sumatranus*

2. Legs spiny but not foliaceous; mesosternum/metasternum with yellow spots; no black band on head of males; pre-anal part of the hind wings in males are greyish brown .... *Pharnacia cantori*
   Legs foliaceous; mesosternum and metasternum without obvious spots; pre-anal part of the hind wings in males are apple green with a white line laterally .... *Pharnacia chiniensis*

Pharnacia cantori (Westwood 1859) (Plate 94 & 95)

Two species of *Pharnacia* are found regularly in the Cameron Highlands. In 1859, Westwood described *Pharnacia cantori* as *Phibalosoma cantori,* p. 74, pl. 37:1, 38:1 (Oxford University Museum no. 621). Brock (1995) subsequently designated the male as the Lectotype. The female thus becomes the paralectotype. *Pharnacia sumatranus* (Brunner von Wattenwyl 1907) of which a female syntype from Sumatra is deposited at the Museum d'Histoire Naturelle, Geneva, Switzerland fits exactly the other species which may be found. This is a new record for this species in West Malaysia. The author has reared and examined a large series of these insects and the two species are thereby separated and redescribed here. The distinguishing features of the two species are that head of both the male and female of *Pharnacia cantori* is elevated and bears two tubercles whereas those of *Pharnacia sumatranus* are flat and do not have tubercles. The males of *Pharnacia sumatranus* have a black band on the side of the head whereas those of *Pharnacia cantori* do not. Males of *Pharnacia sumatranus* are also green whereas males of *Pharnacia cantori* are greyish brown. The mesosternum and metasternum of both sexes of *Pharnacia cantori* are covered with yellow spots whereas those of *Pharnacia sumatranus* are covered with purple spots. The distal end of the hind and mid tibiae of *Pharnacia cantori* are expanded whereas those of *Pharnacia sumatranus* are not obviously flared. The antennae of the females of Pharnacia cantori are longer than the fore femora whereas those of Pharnacia sumatranus are shorter than the fore femora. The eggs of *Pharnacia cantori* are a glossy yellow brown colour whereas those of *Pharnacia sumatranus* are a dull black colour. The nymphs in all instars of *Pharnacia cantori* may be green or brown whereas those of *Pharnacia sumatranus* are green.

FEMALE: 190–230 mm. MALE: 130–145 mm.

The male insect is generally greyish brown and has long wings capable of flight. The antennae reaches to about two-thirds of the way down the front tibiae. The back of the head is raised and bears two tubercles. The sides of the fore and hind wings bears thick white band. The hind wings are greyish brown and just exceeds the 6th abdominal segment. All femora and tibiae are serrated and no subapical spines are present. The ends of the mid and hind tibiae are slightly but distinctly flared. The anal segment is deeply cleft and the cerci are distinct. The mesosternum and metasternum are covered with yellowish spots. The mesonotum and metanotum are smooth and devoid of tubercles. The 7th and 8th abdominal segments are expanded laterally.

The female is a dirty brown wingless insect. Black or green specimens are found occasionally. The fore femora, mid femora, mid tibiae, hind femora and hind tibiae are heavily serrated and spined. The fore tibiae bear less spines but are nonetheless serrated. No subapical spines are present on any of the femora. The ends of the mid and hind tibiae are slightly but distinctly flared. The antennae are longer than the fore femora but shorter than the fore legs. The head is globose and elevated with two tiny tubercles; the left always anterior to the right. The thorax and abdomen are smooth and devoid of spines. The mesosternum and metasternum are covered with yellowish spots. The 7th abdominal segment is expanded laterally. The operculum is boat-shaped and exceeds the anal segment.

FOODPLANT: *Mangifera indica, Psidium guajava, Rubus fruticosus* and *R. moluccanus.*

MEASUREMENTS IN MM

	Male	Female
Total body length	130–145	190–230
Antennae	63–65	54–63
Head	6–6.5	12–14
Pronotum	4–5	8–9
Mesonotum	19–22	35–48
Metanotum	18–20	14–19
Median segment	8–9	11–14
Fore wings	12–14	–

36

Hind wings		73–88	–
Fore-legs:	femur	33–35	45–60
	tibia	40–44	45–60
	tarsus	18–20	19–21
Mid-legs :	femur	28–30	35–44
	tibia	27–31	37–41
	tarsus	10–12	14–17
Hind-legs:	femur	37–40	47–55
	tibia	37–42	40–55
	tarsus	10–13	17–18

Pharnacia sumatranus (Brunner von Wattenwyl 1907) (Plate 93)

FEMALE: 198–225 mm.

The female is a wingless insect which may vary in colour from a bright glossy brown to a brown variegated with white and black. The fore femora, mid femora, mid tibiae, hind femora and hind tibiae are heavily serrated and spined. The fore tibiae bear noticeable serrations. No subapical spines are present on any of the femora. The ends of the mid and hind tibiae are not distinctly flared. The antennae are shorter than the fore femora. The head is flat and does not bear any tubercle. The thorax and abdomen are smooth and devoid of spines. The mesosternum and metasternum are covered with purplish spots. The 7th abdominal segment is expanded laterally. The operculum is boat-shaped and exceeds the anal segment.

MALE: 131–134 mm.

The male insect is a greenish brown winged insect capable of good flight. The antennae reaches to two thirds of the way down the front tibiae. The head is rather flat and has a broad black patch on the sides. No tubercles are present on the head. The mesonotum and metanotum are smooth and devoid of tubercles. The mesosternum and metasternum bears many purple spots. The 7th and 8th abdominal segments are expanded laterally. All the femora and tibiae are serrated. The distal end of all tibiae are not expanded noticeably in anyway. There is a thin white line on the coastal area of the fore and hind wing. which are otherwise greenish. The hind wings are very slightly greenish grey and reaches to the 6th abdominal segment. The anal segment is deeply cleft.

FOODPLANT: *Mangifera indica*, *Psidium guajava*, *Rubus fruticosus* and *R. moluccanus.*

MEASUREMENTS IN MM

	Male	Female
Total body length	131–134	198–225
Antennae	44–45	32–35
Head	6–6.5	12–15
Pronotum	4–4.5	8–8.5
Mesonotum	20–21	37–42

Metanotum		14–15	15–17
Median segment		7	11–12
Fore wings		11–12	–
Hind wings		77	–
Fore-legs:	femur	37	44–53
	tibia	43–45	45–56
	tarsus	14	18–20
Mid-legs:	femur	30–31	38–43
	tibia	28–29	35–40
	tarsus	11–12	12–16
Hind-legs:	femur	37–40	44–51
	tibia	37–38	46–52
	tarsus	12–13	17–19

Pharnacia chiniensis Seow-Choen 1998

FEMALE: 170–205 mm. MALE: 138 mm.
FOODPLANT: *Hopea nutans, Mangifera indica* and *Psidium guajava.*

Key to *Phobaeticus*

1. Smooth thorax; male wings reaches to about 3rd abdominal segment ....
    .... *Phobaeticus serratipes*
    Thorax with some tubercles; wings in males to half of 5th abdominal segment 2

2. Smaller species; mid and hind tarsi broadened not lobed .... *Phobaeticus tirachus*
    Larger species;mid and hind tarsi broadened and lobed .... *Phobaeticus pinnipes*

Phobaeticus serratipes (Gray 1835) (Plate 96)

FEMALE: 235–278 mm. MALE: 127–175 mm.
FOODPLANT: *Macaranga conifera, M. triloba, Mangifera indica, Psidium guajava, Rubus fruticosus* and *R. moluccanus.*

Phobaeticus tirachus (Westwood 1859) (Plate 97)

FEMALE: Unknown. MALE: 115–136 mm.
FOODPLANT: Unknown.

Phobaeticus pinnipes (Redtenbacher 1908)

FEMALE: Unknown. MALE: 163 mm.
FOODPLANT: Unknown.

SUBFAMILY PLATYCRANINAE

Ophicrania flavomaculata Brock 1999 (Plate 98)

FEMALE: Unknown. MALE: 60 mm.
FOODPLANT: Unknown.

Suborder Areolatae

FAMILY BACILLIDAE
SUBFAMILY HETEROPTERYGINAE

Planispectrum bengalensis (Redtenbacher 1906) (Plate 99)

FEMALE: 23–30 mm. MALE: 18.5 mm.
FOODPLANT: *Epipremnum aureum.*

Key to *Pylaemenes*

Head with spines and tufts; spines on thorax and on the 5th abdominal segment in males
.... *Pylaemenes mitratus*
Head with granulations but no spines .... *Pylaemenes mouhotii*

Pylaemenes mouhotii (Bates 1865) (Plate 100)

FEMALE: 45–52 mm. MALE: Unknown.
FOODPLANT: *Curculigo latifolia, Dioscorea glabra, Dracaena fragans, D. godseffiana*
and *Epipremnum aureum.*

Pylaemenes oileus (Westwood 1859) (Plate 101)

Pylaemenes oileus was originally described by Westwood from a female nymph collected from Java. Redtenbacher figured an adult male from Java in Plate 1:15 of his monograph. The present author has collected and reared this species from Mount Gede. Mount Gede is within the Gunung Gede-Pangrango National Park in Java, which is the first official forest reserve in Indonesia and was declared a protected area in 1889. Female nymphs are similar to the nymph figured by Westwood and males are exactly similar to the male of Redtenbacher. *Pylaemenes mitratus* and this taxa from Java are different in external morphology and should be kept as separate species. Gunther (1934: 76) was therefore wrong in synonymizing *Pylaemenes oileus* with *Pylaemenes mitratus*. Females of the Javan species are 36–38.5 mm long and males are 37 mm long. The author has not found *Pylaemenes oileus* in West Malaysia nor Singapore and previous identifications were wrongly assigned. The differences between the two species are that *Pylaemenes mitratus* is bigger and appears wartier. The pronotal, mesonotal and the 5th abdominal segments are more heavily crested than in *Pylaemenes oileus*. The head crest in *Pylaemenes mitratus* also sports an anterior pointing projection which is lacking in *Pylaemenes oileus*. The mid femora of *Pylaemenes oileus* also lacks the white spine which is consistently present one third of the way down the mid femora of females of *Pylaemenes mitratus*. The males of *Pylaemenes mitratus* also bears a pair of spines on the 5th abdominal segment. This is lacking in males of *Pylaemenes oileus*.

Pylaemenes mitratus Redtenbacher 1906 (Plate 102)

FEMALE: 47–48 mm. MALE: 37–43 mm.
FOODPLANT: *Aidia wallichiana, Curculigo latifolia, Daemonorops cf didymorphylla, Dieffenbachia sp., Dracaena fragans, D. godseffiana, Epipremnum aureum, Rubus fruticosus, Uncaria gambir, Urophyllum glabrum.*

Haaniella muelleri (de Haan 1842) (Plate 103 & 104)

FEMALE: 97–110 mm. MALE: 66–78 mm.
FOODPLANT: *Mangifera indica, Psidium guajava, Rubus fruticosus* and *R. moluccanus.*

Heteropteryx dilatata (Parkinson 1798) (Plate 105 & 106)

FEMALE: 145–150 mm. MALE: 80–102 mm.
FOODPLANT: *Durio zibeththinus, Eugenia aquea* (with reluctance), *Grewia acuminata, Manihot esculenta, Psidium guajava, Rubus moluccanus* and *Uncaria* spp.

Gynandromorphs are more commonly seen in this species than in most other phasmids and two specimens in the authors' collection are illustrated (Plate 107).

FAMILY PSEUDOPHASMATIDAE
SUBFAMILY ASCHIPHASMATINAE

Key to *Abrosoma*

1. Greenish-brown species; hind wings brown .... *Abrosoma xiuyuae*
   Brown-black species; may/may not possess wings 2

2. Wings in males; females wingless; mesothorax without humps .. *Abrosoma johorensis*
   Neither sex possessing wings 3

3. Mesothorax without humps .... *Abrosoma festinatum*
   Mesothorax with central hump towards back; abdomen with two or more humps ....
   .... *Abrosoma gibberum*

Abrosoma festinatum Brock & Seow-Choen 1995 (Plate 108)

FEMALE: 40–48 mm. MALE: 28–37 mm.
FOODPLANT: *Clidemia hirta, Leea indica* and *Melastoma malabathricum.*

Abrosoma gibberum Brock & Seow-Choen 1995 (Plate 109)

FEMALE: 29–30 mm. MALE: 18.3 mm.
FOODPLANT: *Clidemia hirta* and *Melastoma malabathricum.*

Abrosoma xiuyuae Brock & Seow-Choen 1999 (Plate 110)

FEMALE: 49–52 mm. MALE: 33–37 mm.
FOODPLANT: *Pternandra echinata.*

Abrosoma johorensis Seow-Choen & Goh 1999 (Plate 111)

FEMALE: 42–47 mm. MALE: 32–36 mm
FOODPLANT: *Clidemia hirta, Leea indica* and *Melastoma malabathricum.*

Aschiphasma annulipes Westwood 1830 (Plate 112)

FEMALE: 69–72 mm. MALE: 53–58 mm.
FOODPLANT: Unknown.

Pinnispinus harmani Brock 1995 (Plate 113)

FEMALE: 28–33 mm. MALE: 18–21 mm.
FOODPLANT: *Rubus fruticosus.*

Key to *Presbistus*

1. Hind wings pink; thorax and pre-anal part of hind wings light green; 3 ocelli present
    .... *Presbistus fragilis*
    Hind wings not pink 2

2. Hind wings orangy with a darker border; thorax and pre-anal part of the hind wings
    brown with white spots .... *Presbistus horni*
    Hind wings brown 3

3. Pre-anal part of the hind wings with white spots 4
    Pre-anal part of the hind wings plain with green veins, fore wing spine black;
    undersurface of mid and hind femora with small spines ....
    .... *Presbistus eryx*

4. End of anal segment beak shaped in males; large black spur between anal segment
    and operculum in both sexes .... *Presbistus peleus*
    End of anal segment divided into 2 lobes; black spur not present; fore wing spine dark
    brown with black tip .... *Presbistus flavicornis*

Presbistus peleus (Gray 1835) (Plate 114)

FEMALE: 46–54 mm. MALE: 40–46 mm.
FOODPLANT: *Cayrata japonica, Cissus repens, Leea indica* and *Tetrastigma
pedunculare.*
This species may be found in Sarawak as well.

Presbistus flavicornis (de Haan 1842) (Plate 115)

FEMALE: 47–55 mm. MALE: 44–47 mm.
FOODPLANT: Unknown.

Presbistus horni (Redtenbacher 1908) (Plate 116)

FEMALE: 44–47 mm. MALE: 34 mm.
FOODPLANT: Unknown.

Presbistus eryx (Westwood 1859) (Plate 117)

MALE: 37 mm.
FOODPLANT: Unknown.

Presbistus fragilis Seow-Choen sp. nov. (Plate 118)

This rare species has been found only on Gunong Jerai in Kedah and in the Forest Recreation Reserve in Melaka. The male is a small winged insect. Unfortunately the female has not been found to date. The insect has a generally green coloration. The prothorax and mesothorax are light apple green. The head may be slightly brownish green with three prominent ocelli. The eyes are very large and dark brown. The fore femora are reddish green whereas the mid and hind femora are light apple green. The coastal areas of the hind wings are light greenish and slightly transparent showing the light pinkish colour of the membranous hind wings when folded at rest. The fore wings are much reduced and are spine-like or crescent shaped with a greenish base and brown tip. The anal segment is deeply incised triangularly.

HOLOTYPE: Male. West Malaysia, Kedah, Gunung Jerai, 20.II.96. F. Seow-Choen & Joseph Koh (in The Zoological Reference Collection, National University of Singapore).

PARATYPES: 2 males. West Malaysia, One: Kedah, Gunung Jerai, 21.II.96. F. Seow-Choen & Joseph Koh; one: Melaka, Forest Recreation Reserve, 7. IX.98, F. Seow-Choen, I. Seow-En & S. Seow-An (in the collection of F. Seow-Choen).

MEASUREMENTS IN MM

		Male
Total body length		43–50
Antennae		40–46
Head		2
Pronotum		1.5–2
Mesonotum		6.5
Metanotum		2
Median segment		3
Fore wings		spine-like
Hind wings		27
Fore-legs:	femur	13–14
	tibia	12–13
	tarsus	8–8.5
Mid-legs :	femur	9
	tibia	7–8
	tarsus	4–5
Hind-legs:	femur	13
	tibia	13–14
	tarsus	6–7

Presbistus sp. 1 (unidentified) (Plate 119)

MALE: 42 mm.
Found at Genting Highlands.

Presbistus sp. 2 (unidentified) (Plate 120)

MALE: 43 mm.
Found at Rifle Range Road, Singapore.

SUBFAMILY KORINNINAE

Kalocorinnis pulchella (de Haan 1842) (Plate 121)

FEMALE: 38 mm. MALE: 28–30 mm.
FOODPLANT: Unknown.

FAMILY PHYLLIDAE

Key to *Phyllium*

1. Abdominal segments 8 onwards tapered towards anal segment 2
    Abdominal segments lobed 3

2. Fore femur without large posterior lobe; eggs hairy in appearance ....
    .... *Phyllium siccifolium*
    Fore femur with large posterior lobe; eggs star-shaped .... *Phyllium bioculatum*

3. Margins of abdominal segment 8 incurved; large species; eggs are black ....
    .... *Phyllium giganteum*
    Margins of abdominal segment 8 lobed not excavated 4

4. Abdominal segment 8-lobed; egg star-shaped .... *Phyllium pulchrifolium*
    Abdominal segments 7–8 strongly lobed .... *Phyllium hausleithneri*

Phyllium siccifolium (Linnaeus 1758) (Plate 122)

FEMALE: 77–92 mm. MALE: 53–67 mm.
FOODPLANT: *Mangifera indica*, *Nephilium lappaceum* and *Psidium guajava*.

Phyllium bioculatum Gray 1832 (Plate 123)

FEMALE: 67–94 mm. Male: 46–68.
FOODPLANT: *Mangifera indica, Nephilium lappaceum* and *Psidium guajava.*

Phyllium pulchrifolium Audinet-Serville 1838 (Plate 124)

Brock synomymized *P. pulchrifolium* and *P. bioculatum* but expressed doubts nevertheless regarding whether indeed they were one species (Brock 1999).

FEMALE: 68–92 mm. MALE: 46–63 mm.
FOODPLANT: *Mangifera indica, Nephilium lappaceum* and *Psidium guajava.*

Phyllium giganteum Hausleithner 1984 (Plate 125 & 126)

FEMALE: 98–114 mm. MALE: 80–81 mm.
FOODPLANT: *Mangifera indica, Nephilium lappaceum, Psidium guajava* and *Saraca thaipingensis.*

Phyllium hausleithneri Brock 1999 (Plate 127)

FEMALE: 77–82 mm. MALE: Unknown.
FOODPLANT: *Mangifera indica.*

Plate 1

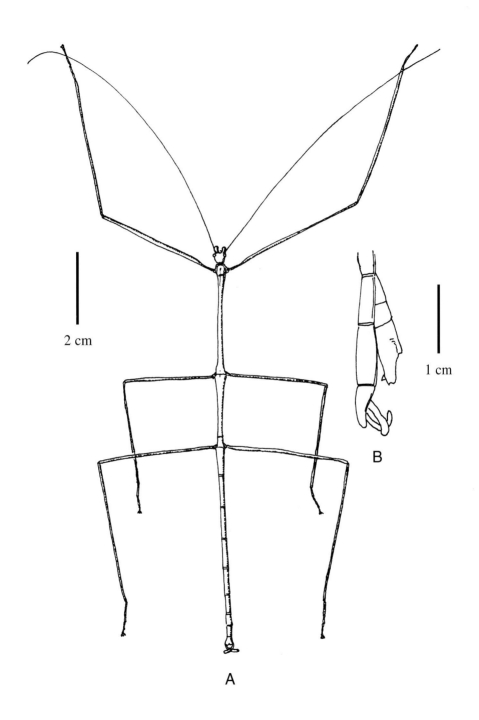

A. Holotype (male) of *Pseudobactricia ridleyi* (Kirby 1904). B. An enlarged sketch showing the end abdominal segments (after Brock).

Plate 2

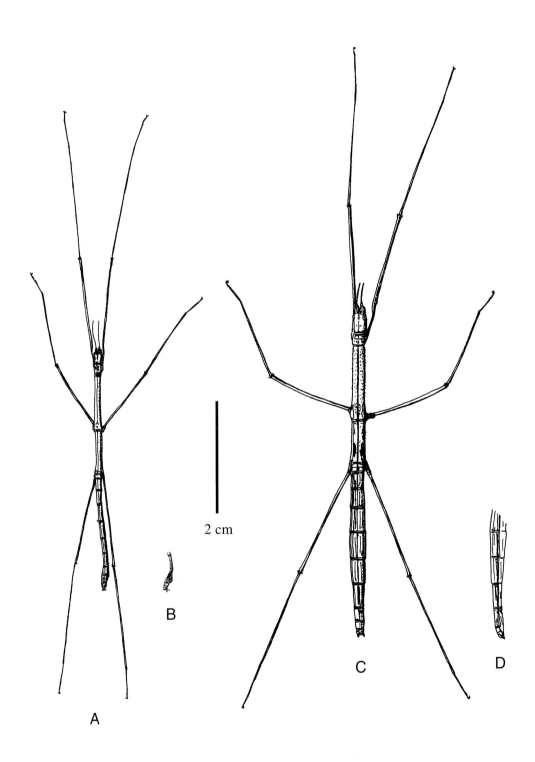

2 cm

A

B

C

D

Sceptrophasma langkawicensis Brock & Seow-Choen gen. et sp. nov. A & B. Male and end abdominal segments. C & D. Female end abdominal segments.

Plate 3

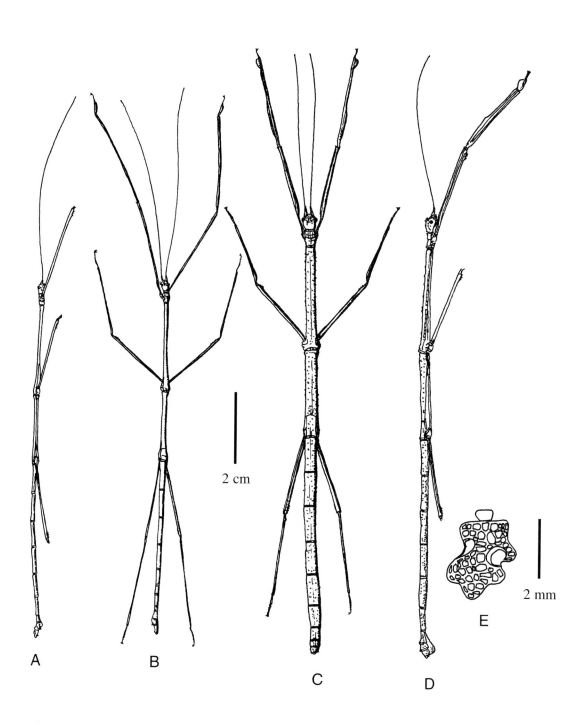

Carausius crawangensis (de Haan 1842). A & B. Male. C & D. Female. E. Egg.

Plate 4

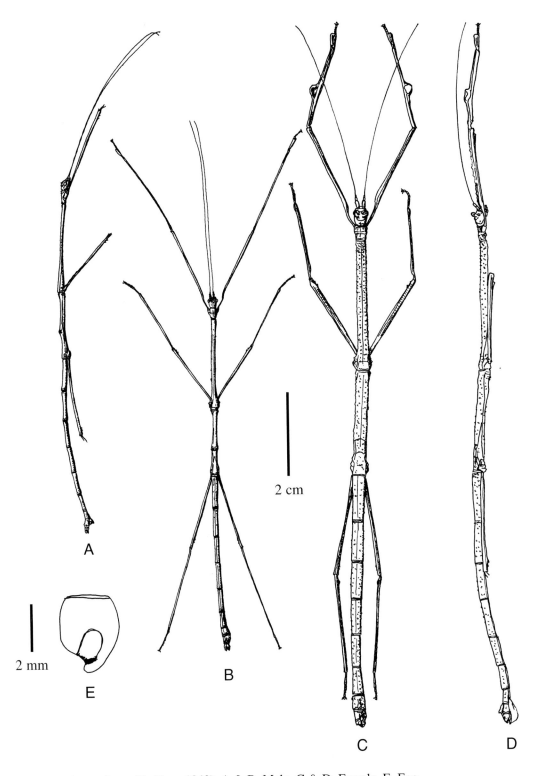

2 cm

2 mm

A

B

C

D

E

Carausius nodosus (de Haan 1842). A & B. Male. C & D. Female. E. Egg.

Plate 5

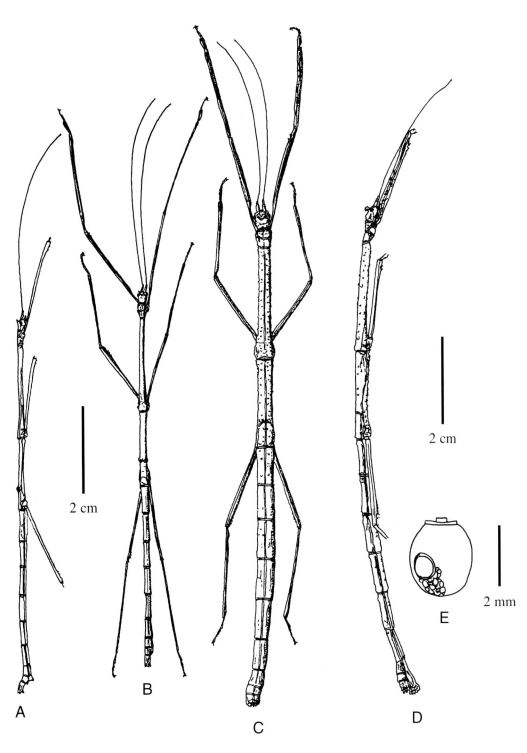

Carausius tanahrataensis Seow-Choen sp. nov. A & B. Male. C & D. Female. E. Egg.

Plate 6

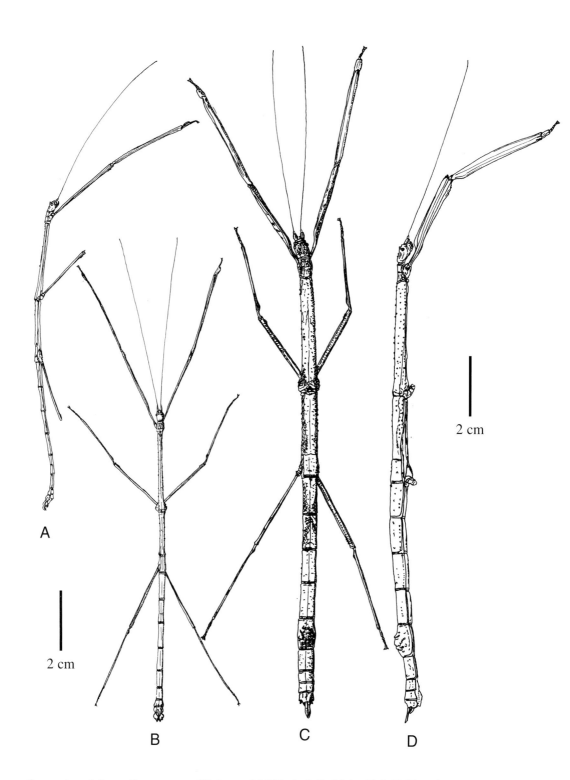

A

2 cm

B

C

D

2 cm

Carausius globosus Brunner von Wattenwyl 1907. A & B. Male. C & D. Female.

Plate 7

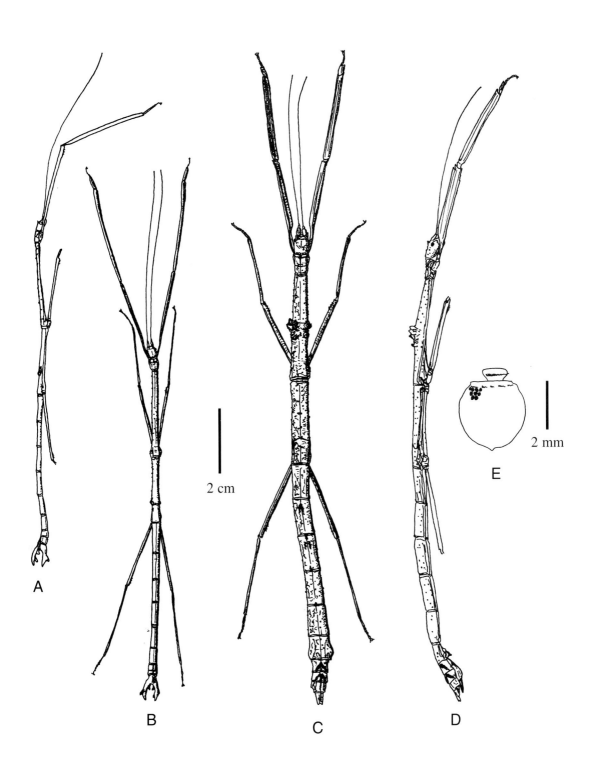

2 cm

2 mm

A

B

C

D

E

Carausius spinosus Brunner von Wattenwyl 1907. A & B. Male. C & D. Female. E. Egg.

Plate 8

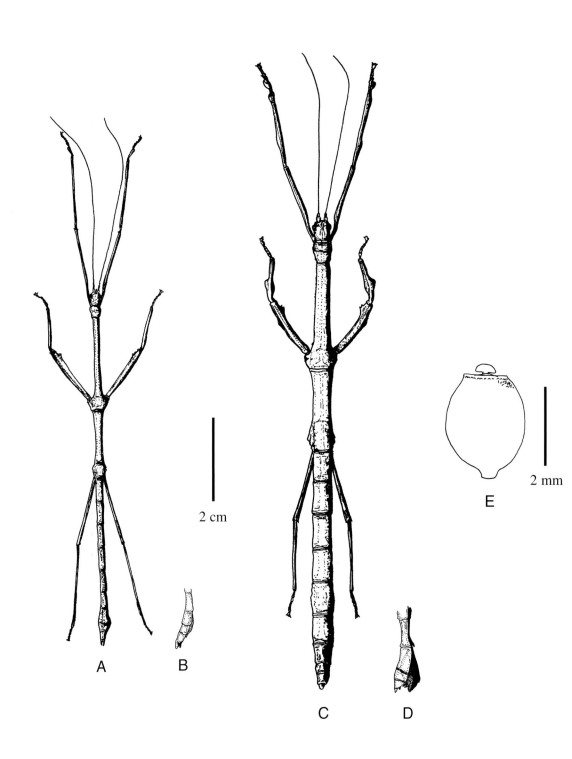

2 cm

2 mm

A   B

C   D   E

Lonchodes brevipes Gray 1835, from Singapore. A & B. Male. C & D. Female. E. Egg.

Plate 9

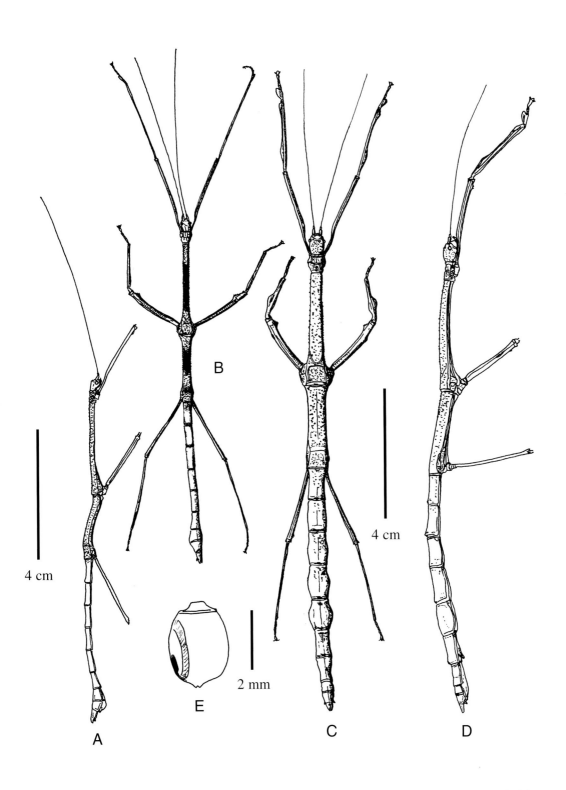

Lonchodes brevipes Gray 1835, from Peninsular Malaysia. A & B. Male. C & D. Female. E. Egg.

Plate 10

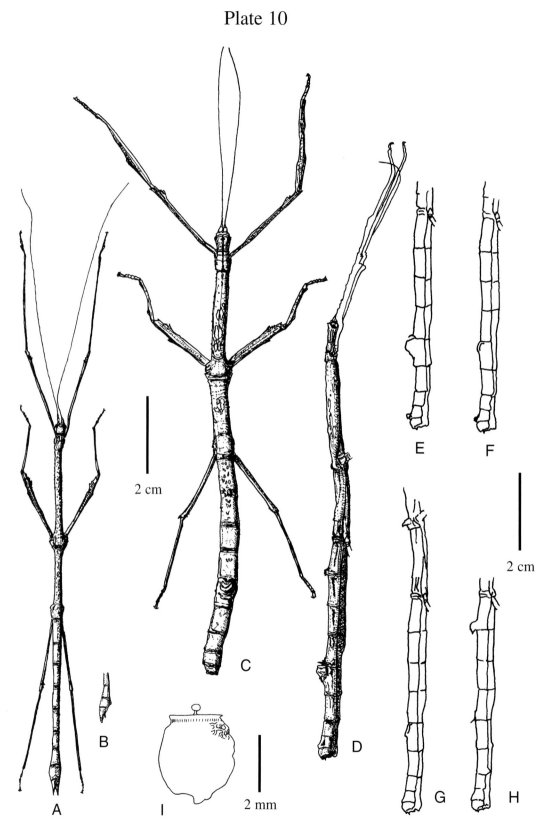

Lonchodes geniculatus Gray 1835. A & B. Male. C & D. Female. E–H. Shows the variations in abdominal warts and spines. I. Egg.

Plate 11

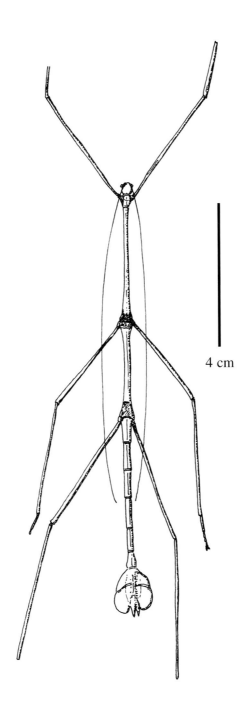

4 cm

Lonchodes skapanus Brock 1999. Holotype male.

Plate 12

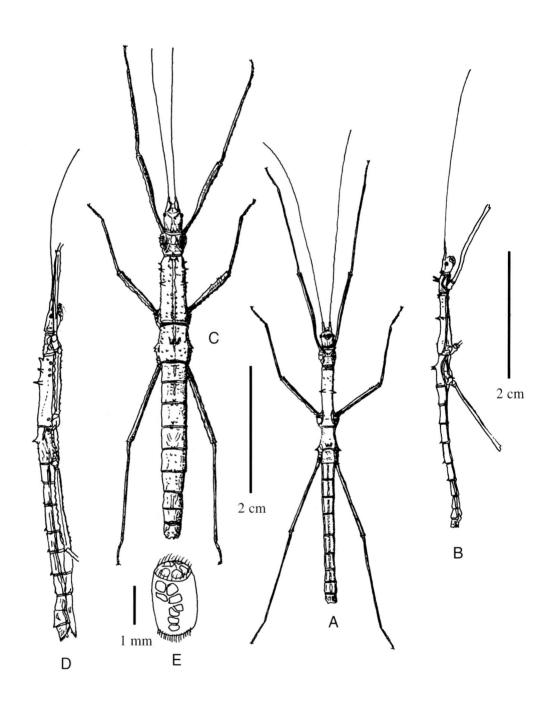

2 cm

2 cm

1 mm

C

D

E

A

B

Menexenus unnoi Brock 1999. A & B. Male. C & D. Female. E. Egg.

Plate 13

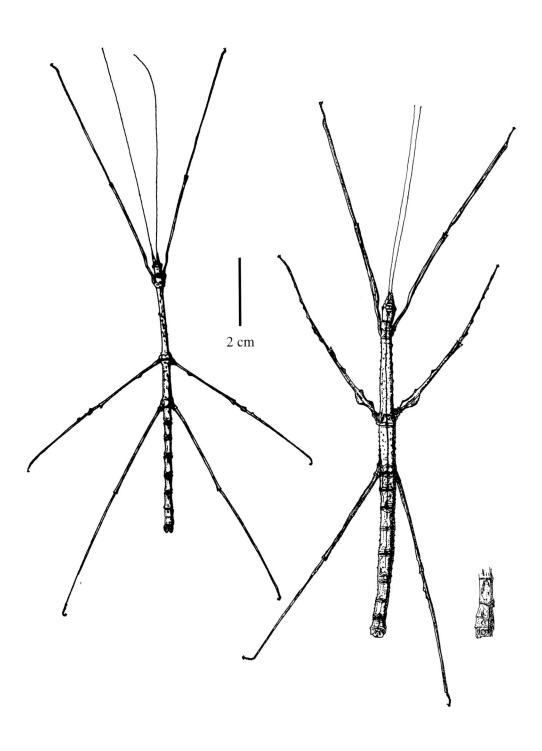

2 cm

Prisomera malaya (Stål 1875). A. Male. B & C. Female.

Plate 14

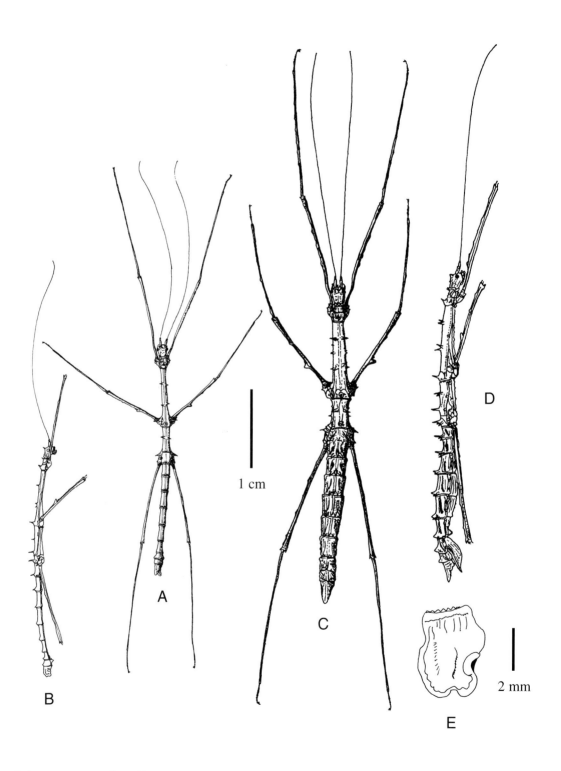

1 cm

2 mm

A

B

C

D

E

Prisomera verruculosa (Brunner von Wattenwyl 1907), from Tapah Hills. A & B. Male. C & D. Female. E. Egg.

Plate 15

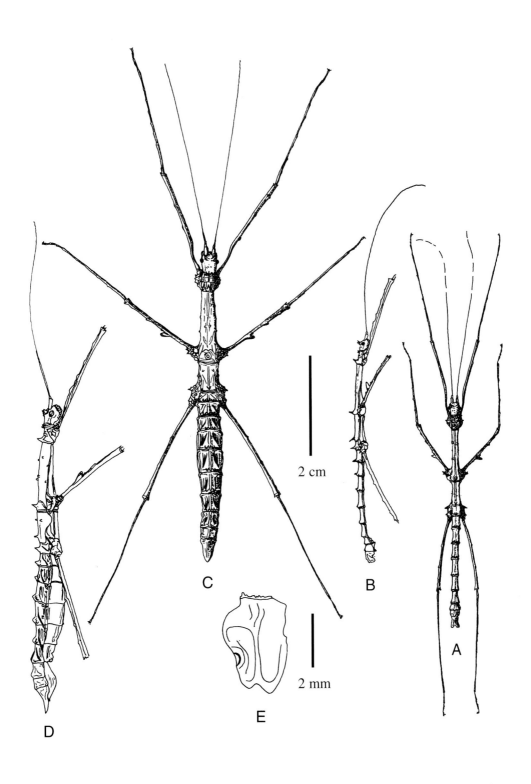

2 cm

C

B

A

2 mm

E

D

Prisomera verruculosa (Brunner von Wattenwyl 1907), from Tanah Rata. A & B. Male. C & D. Female. E. Egg.

Plate 16

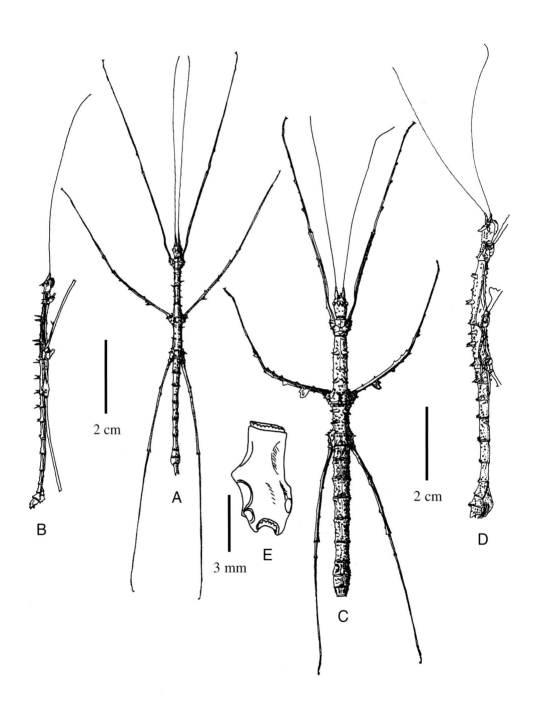

2 cm

3 mm

2 cm

A

B

C

D

E

Prisomera repudiosa (Brunner von Wattenwyl 1907). A & B. Male. C & D. Female. E. Egg.

Plate 17

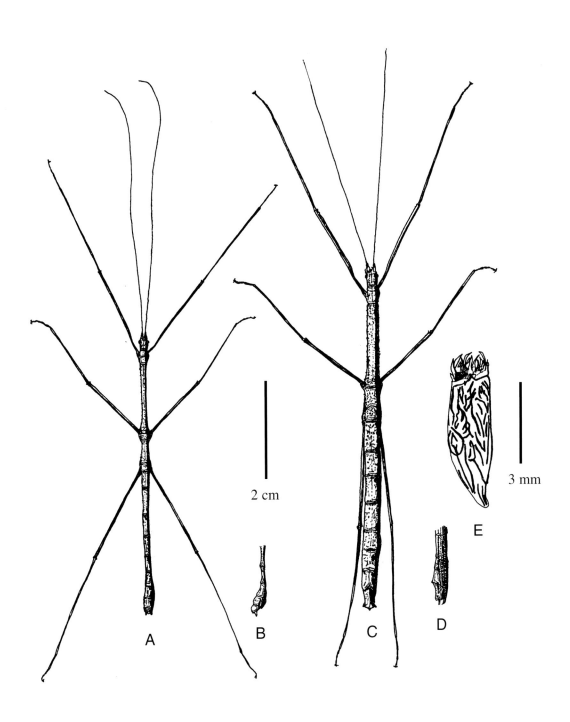

Acacus sarawacus (Westwood 1859). A & B. Male. C & D. Female. E. Egg.

Plate 18

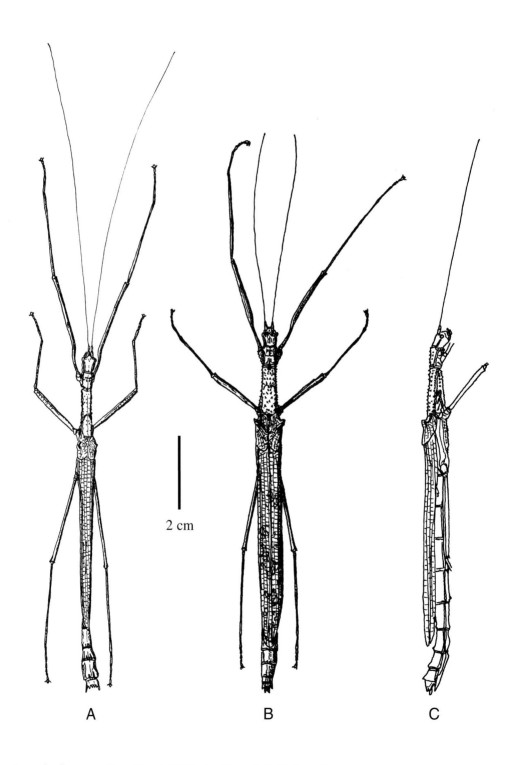

2 cm

A   B   C

Anarchodes magnificus Brock 1999. A. Male. B & C. Female.

Plate 19

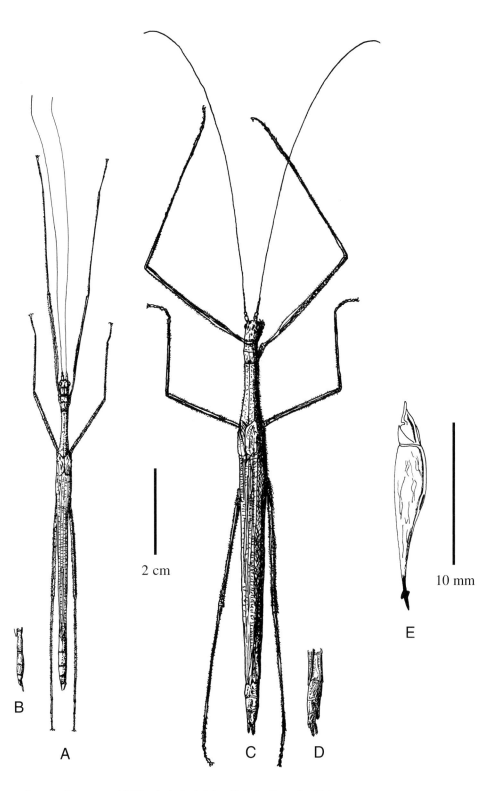

Asceles malaccae (Saussure 1868). A & B. Male. C & D. Female. E. Egg.

Plate 20

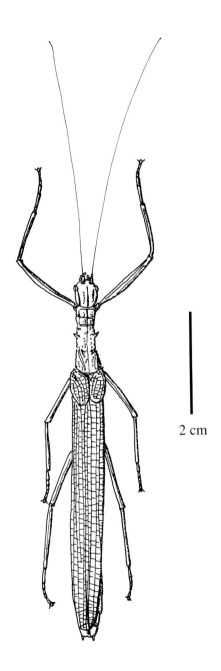

2 cm

Asceles brevicollis Redtenbacher 1908. Female.

Plate 21

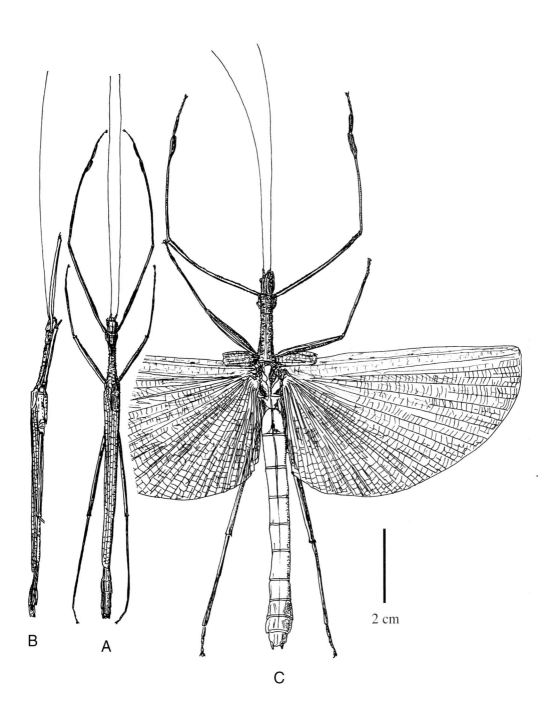

Asceles validus Redtenbacher 1908. A & B. Male. C. Female.

Plate 22

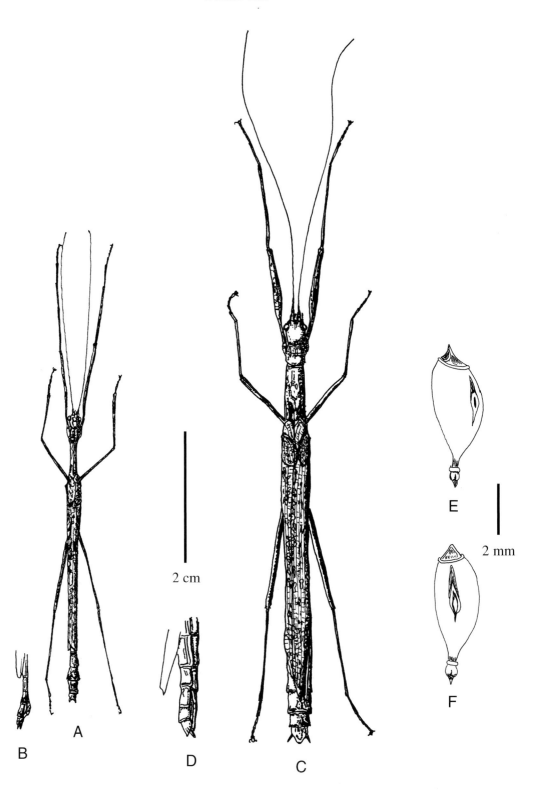

2 cm

2 mm

A

B

D

C

E

F

Asceles larunda (Westwood 1859). A & B. Male. C & D. Female. E & F. Egg.

Plate 23

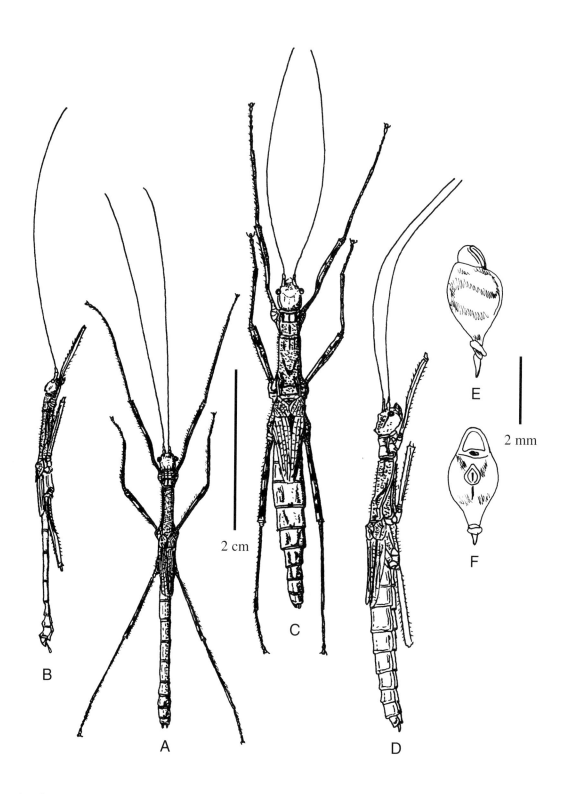

2 cm

2 mm

Asceles tanarata Brock 1999. A & B. Male. C & D. Female. E & F. Egg.

Plate 24

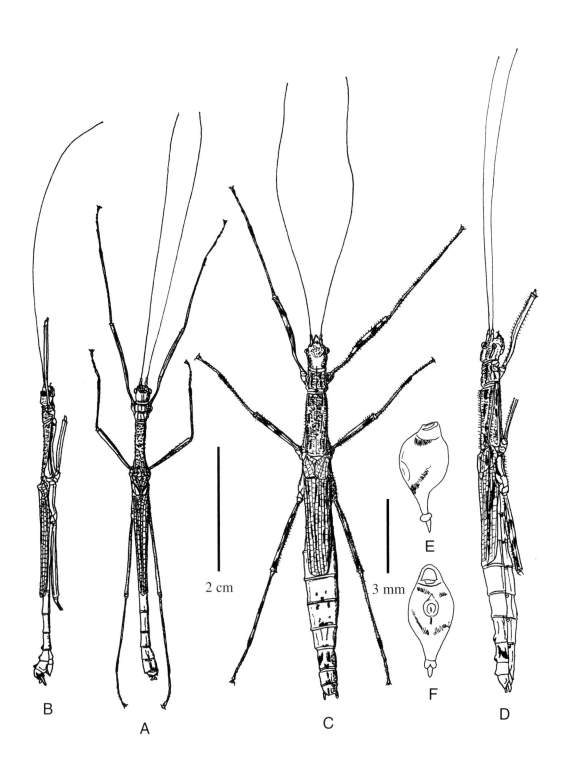

Asceles tanarata amplior Brock 1999. A & B. Male. C & D. Female. E & F. Egg.

Plate 25

Asceles tanarata singapura Seow-Choen & Brock 1999 comb. subsp. nov. A & B. Male. C & D. Female. E. Egg.

Plate 26

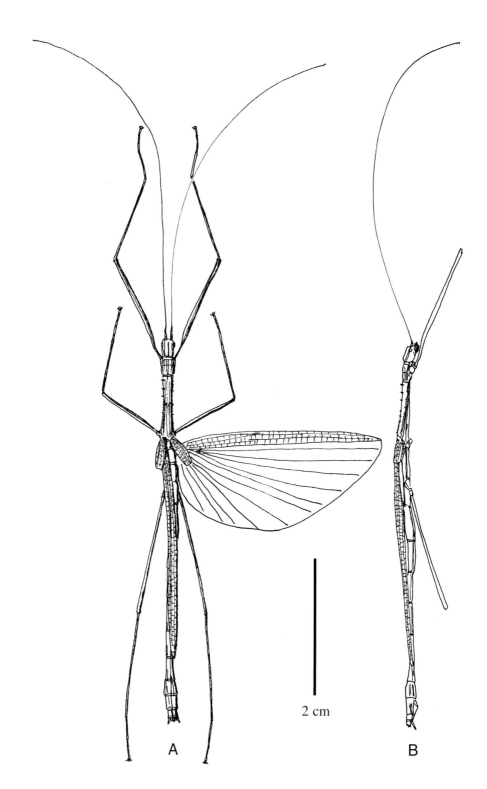

2 cm

A   B

Asceles sp 1 (unidentified) from Tapah Hills. A & B. Male.

Plate 27

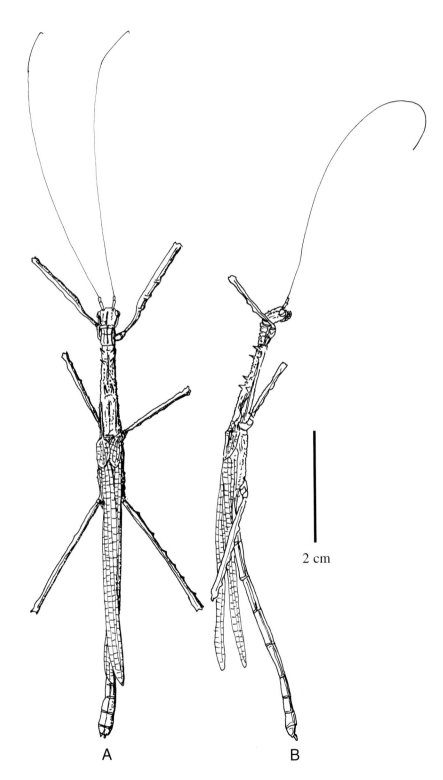

Asceles sp 2 (unidentified) from Bangi Forest, Selangor. A & B. Male.

Plate 28

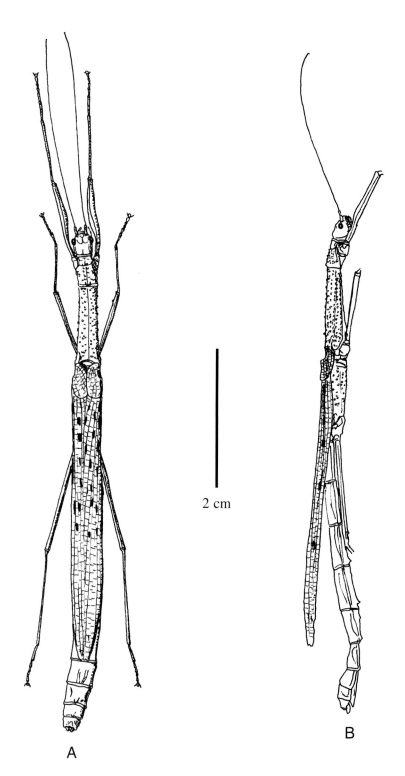

A

B

Asceles sp 3 (unidentified) from Tapah Hills.. A & B. Female.

Plate 29

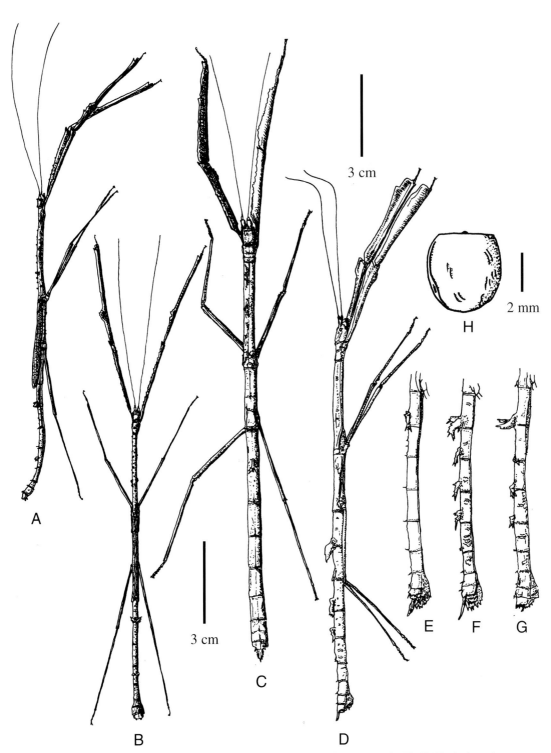

Baculofractum insignis (Brunner 1907). A & B. Male. C & D. Female. E–G. Variations in abdominal outgrowths. H. Egg.

Plate 30

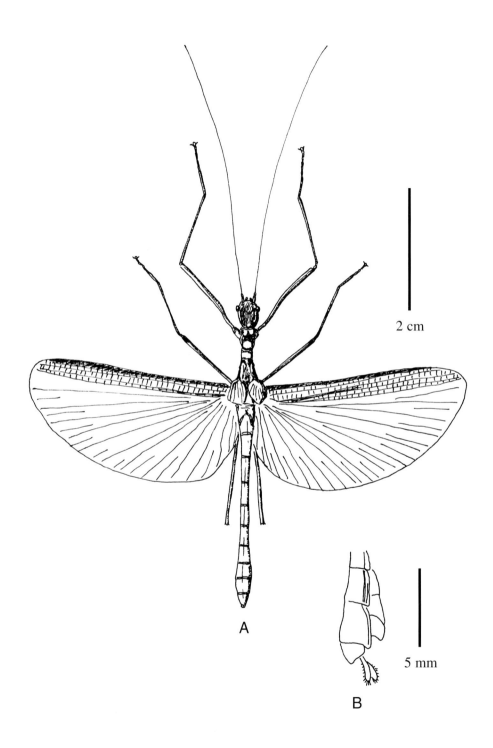

Calvisia hemus (Westwood 1859). A. Female. B. Lateral view of genitalia.

Plate 31

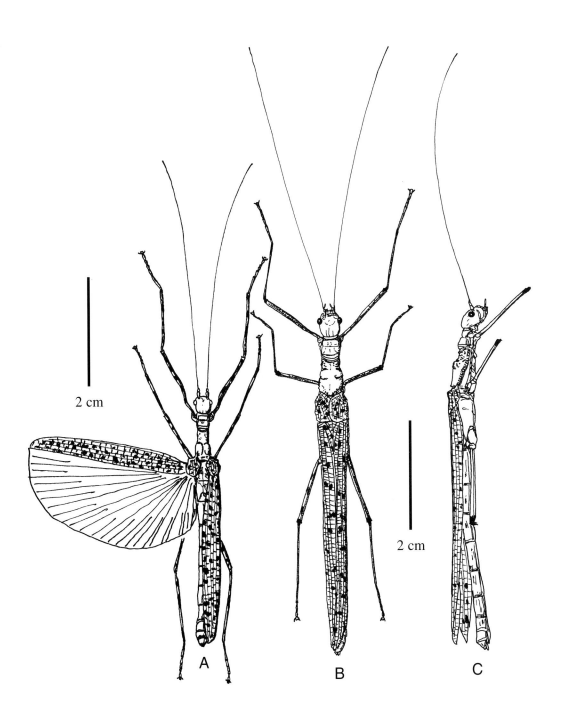

2 cm

2 cm

A

B

C

Calvisia sangarius (Westwood 1859). A. Male. B & C. Female.

Plate 32

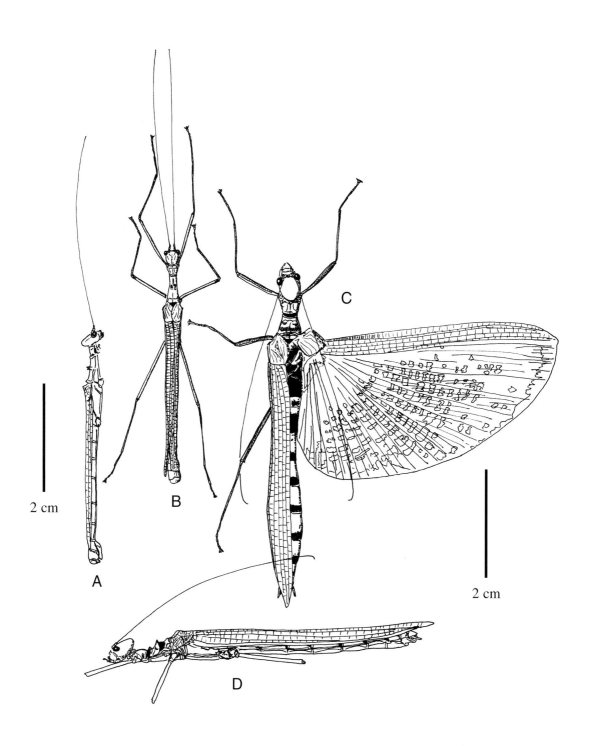

2 cm

2 cm

A

B

C

D

Calvisia virbius (Westwood 1859). A & B. Male. C & D. Female.

Plate 33

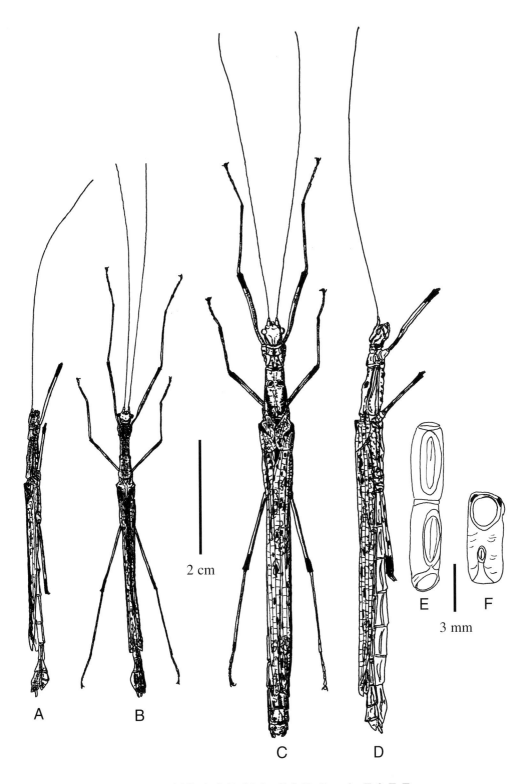

2 cm

E   F

3 mm

Calvisia conicipennis (Bates 1865). A & B. Male. C & D. Female. E & F. Eggs.

Plate 34

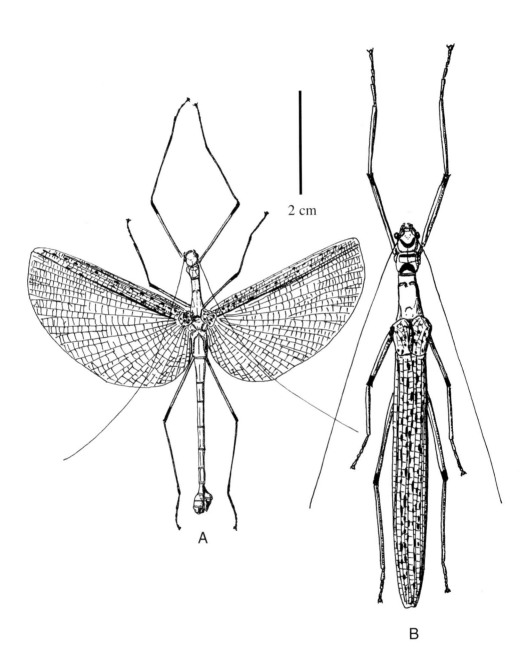

2 cm

A

B

Calvisia clarissima Redtenbacher 1908. A. Male. B. Female.

Plate 35

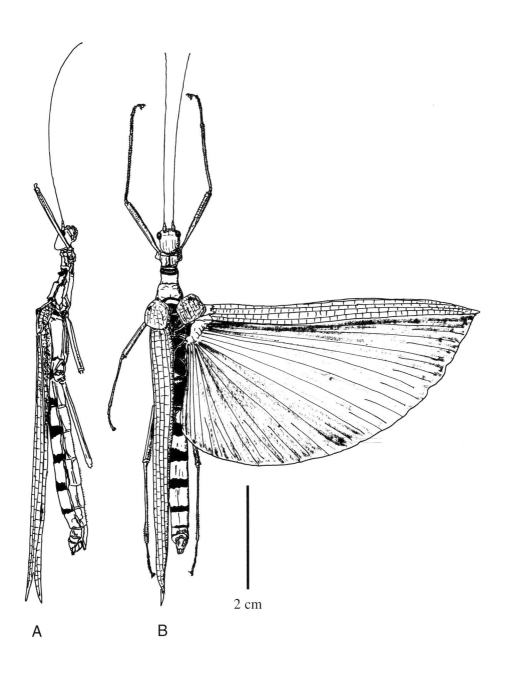

A   B

2 cm

Calvisia coerulescens Redtenbacher 1908. A & B. Female.

Plate 36

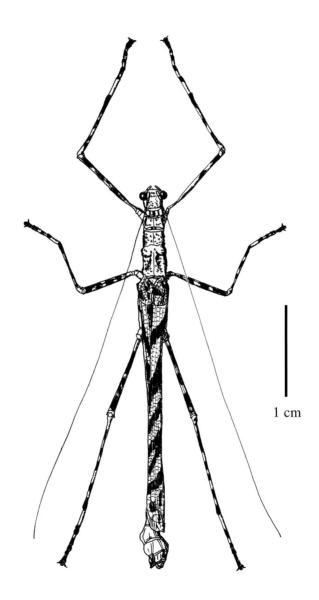

1 cm

Calvisia medora (Westwood 1859). Male.

Plate 37

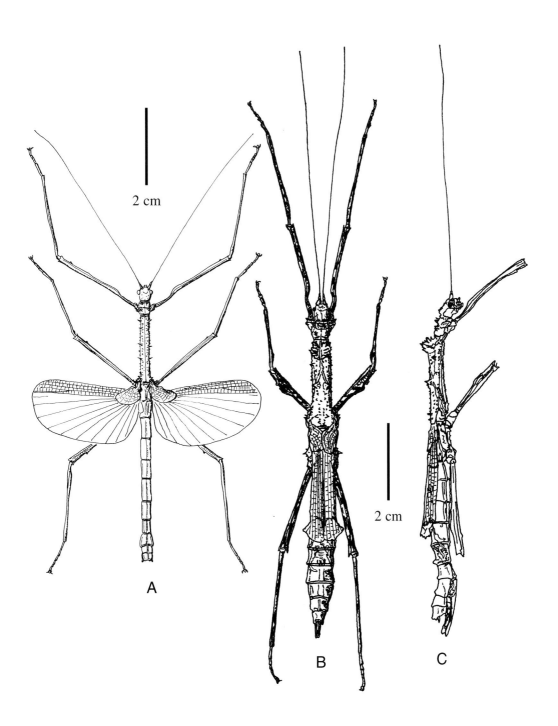

2 cm

2 cm

A

B

C

Centrophasma spinosum (Saussure 1868). A. Male. B & C. Female.

Plate 38

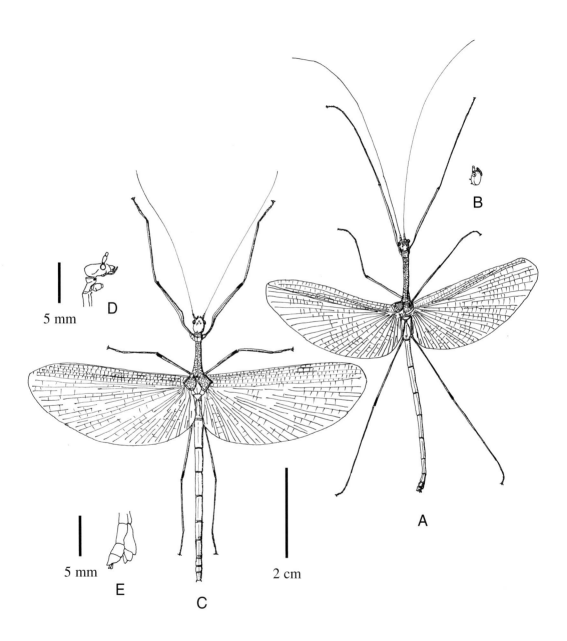

Diacanthoidea diacanthos (de Haan 1842). A & B. Male. C & D. Female. E. End abdominal segments of female.

Plate 39

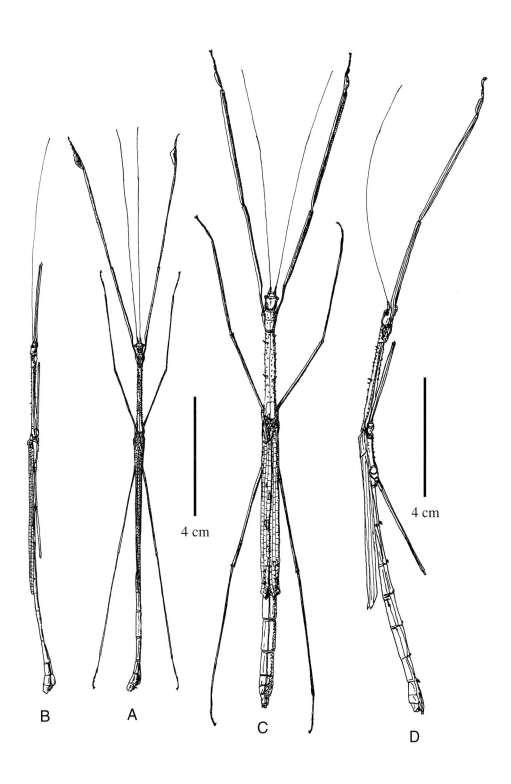

Diardia diardi (de Haan 1842) from Sarawak. A& B. Male. C & D. Female.

Plate 40

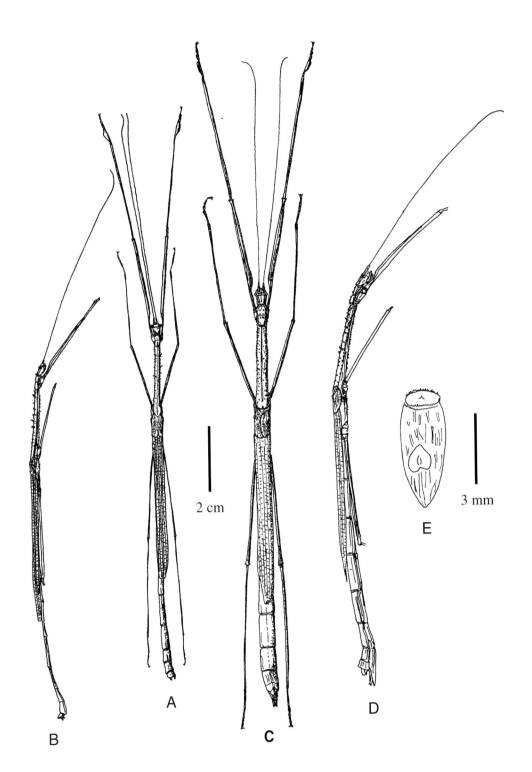

A

B

C

D

E

Diardia diardi (de Haan 1842) West Malaysian. A & B. Male. C & D. Female. E. Egg.

2 cm

3 mm

Plate 41

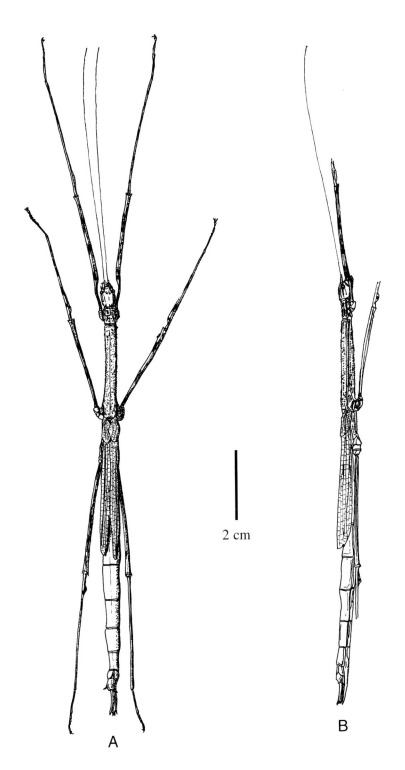

2 cm

A

B

Diardia palliata Redtenbacher 1908. A & B. Female.

Plate 42

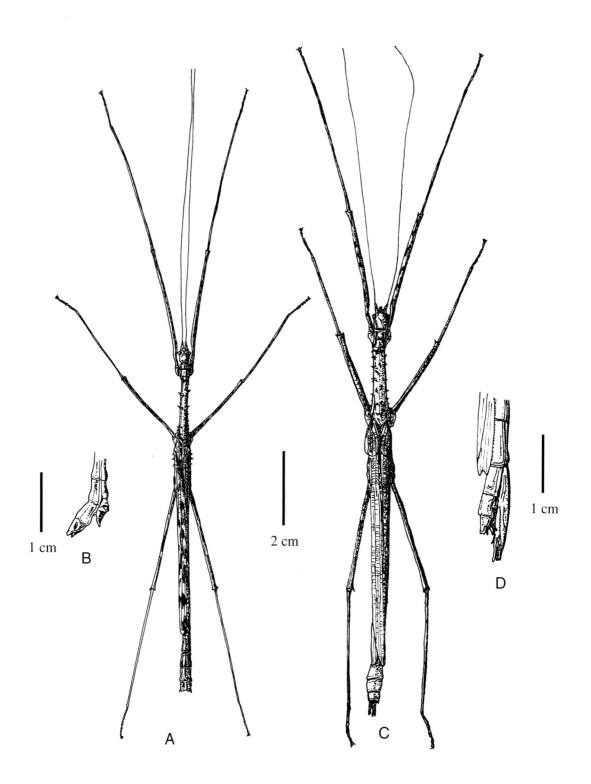

1 cm

B

2 cm

1 cm

D

A

C

Diesbachia tamyris (Westwood 1859). A & B. Male. C & D. Female.

Plate 43

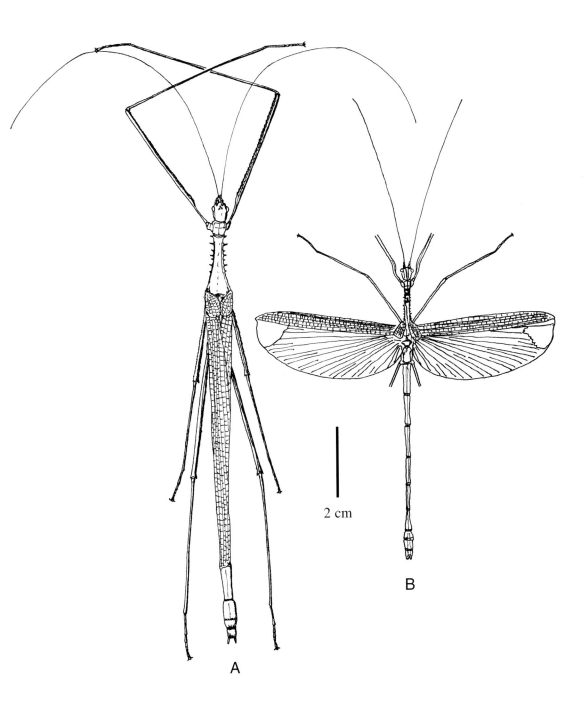

2 cm

A

B

Gargantuoidea phaetusa (Westwood 1859). A. Male (after Westwood). B. Female.

Plate 44

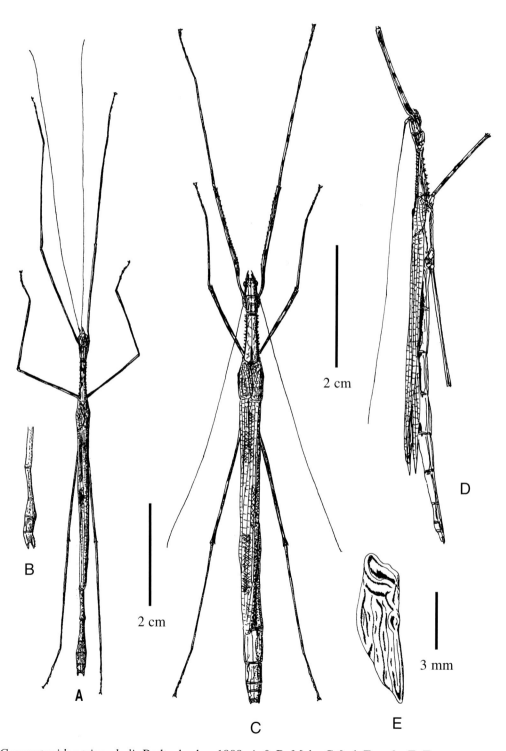

2 cm

2 cm

3 mm

A

B

C

D

E

Gargantuoidea triumphalis Redtenbacher 1908. A & B. Male. C & d. Female. E. Egg.

Plate 45

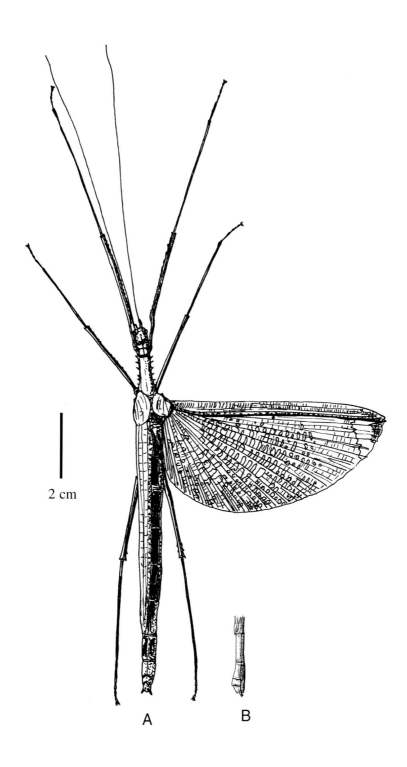

2 cm

A   B

Gargantuoidea tessellata Redtenbacher 1908. A & B. Female.

Plate 46

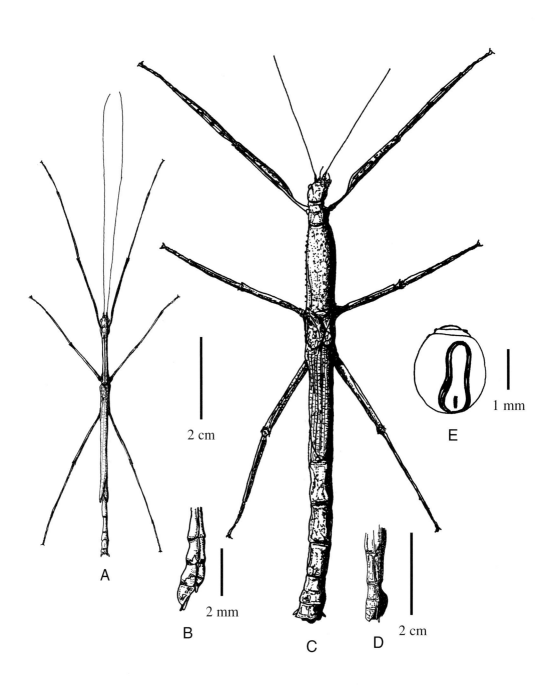

2 cm

1 mm

E

A

B

2 mm

C

D

2 cm

Lopaphus brachypterus (de Haan 1842). A & B. Male. C & D. Female. E. Egg.

Plate 47

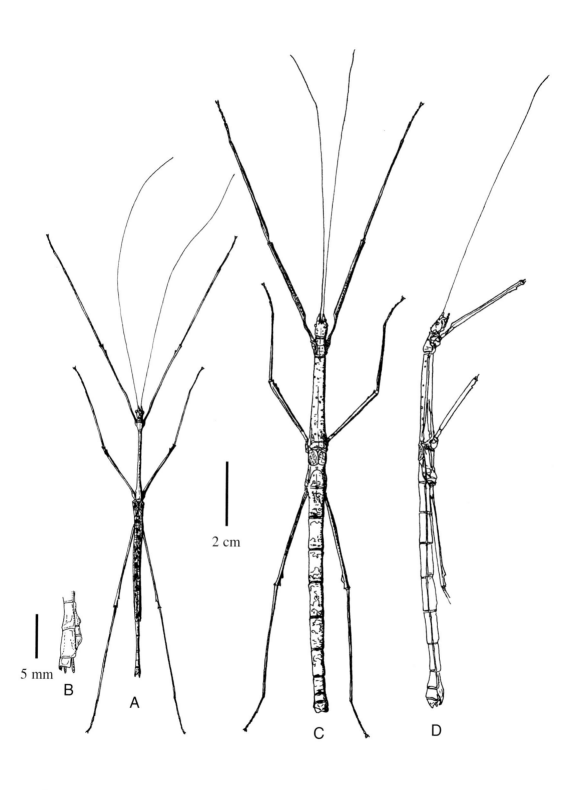

5 mm

2 cm

B

A

C

D

Lopaphus iolas (Westwood 1859) from Singapore, Tasek Chini, and Johore. A & B. Male. C & D. Female.

Plate 48

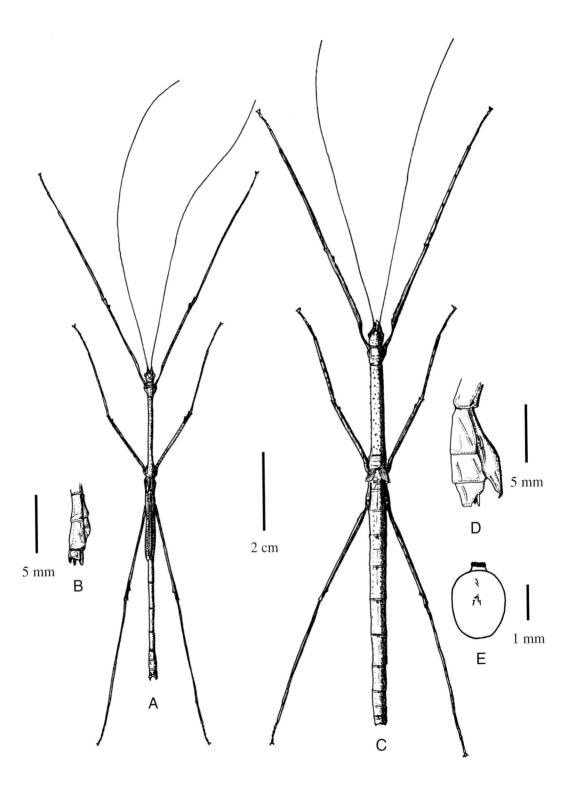

Lopaphus iolas (Westwood 1859), Gombak, Kepong, Peninsular Malaysia. A. Female, top view. B. Apex of abdomen. C. Male, top view. D. Apex of abdomen. E. Egg.

Plate 49

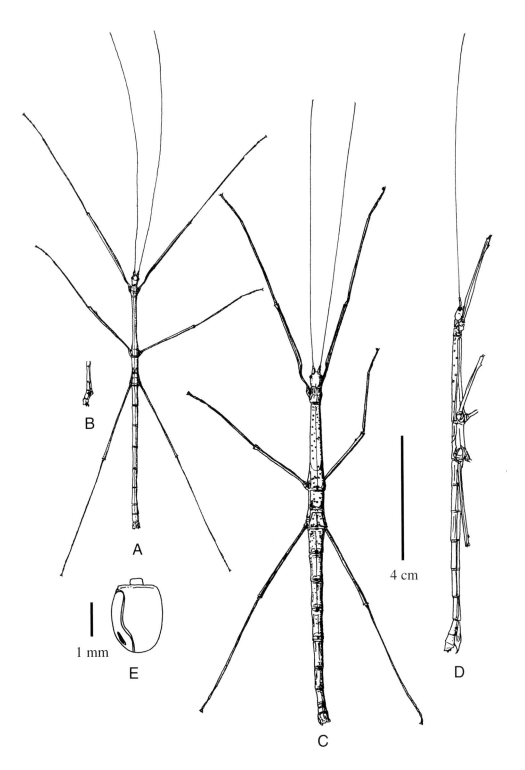

Lopaphus iolas (Westwood 1859) Kedah Peak. A & B. Male from Gombak. C & D. Female from Kedah Peak.

Plate 50

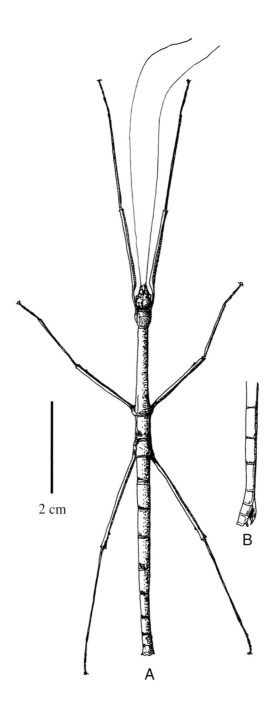

2 cm

A

B

Lopaphus perakensis (Redtenbacher 1908). A & B. Female.

Plate 51

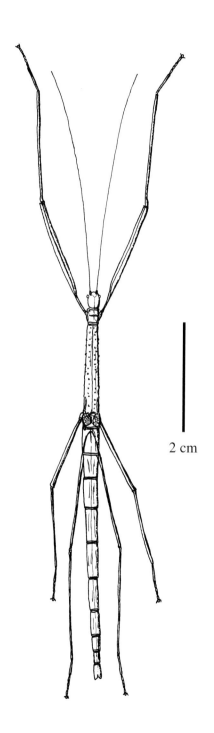

2 cm

Lopaphus nanoalatus Brock 1999. Female (after Brock).

Plate 52

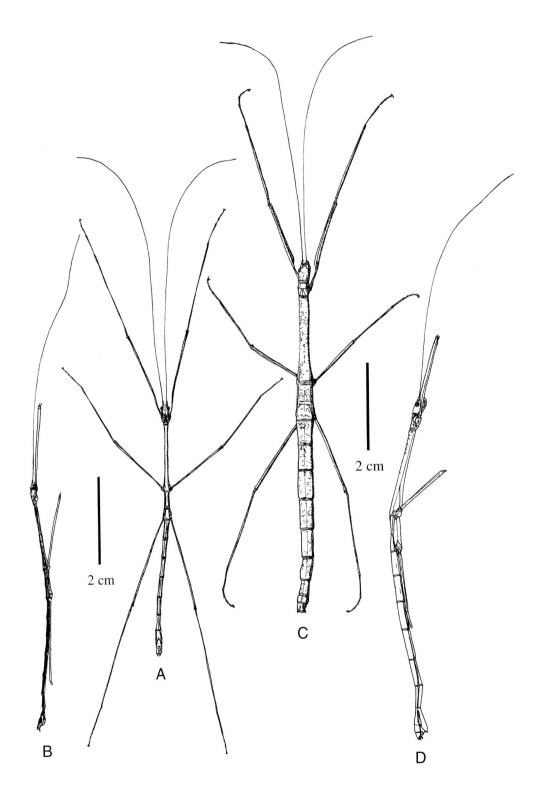

2 cm

2 cm

A

B

C

D

Lopaphus suwinae Seow-Choen sp. nov. A & B. Male. C & D. Female.

Plate 53

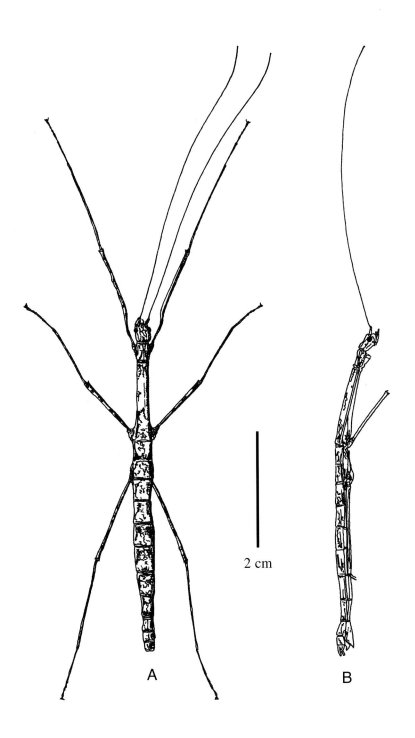

2 cm

A

B

Lopaphus sp. (unidentified) from Tanah Rata, Cameron Highlands. A & B. Female.

Plate 54

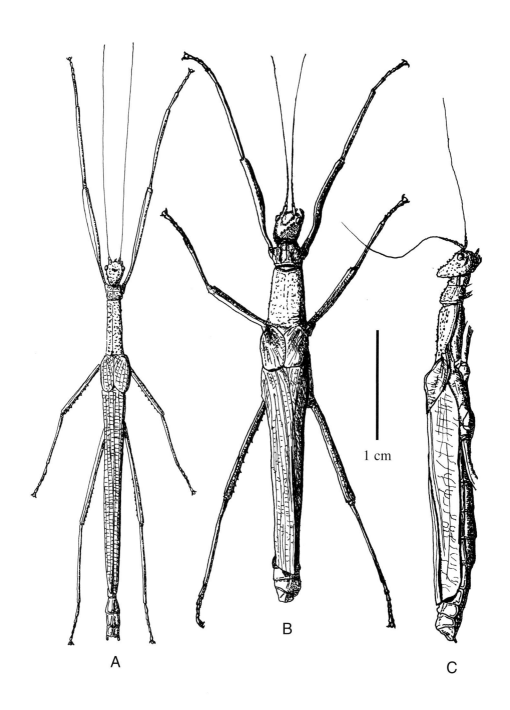

1 cm

A

B

C

Loxopsis seowi Brock 1999. A. Male. B & C. Female.

Plate 55

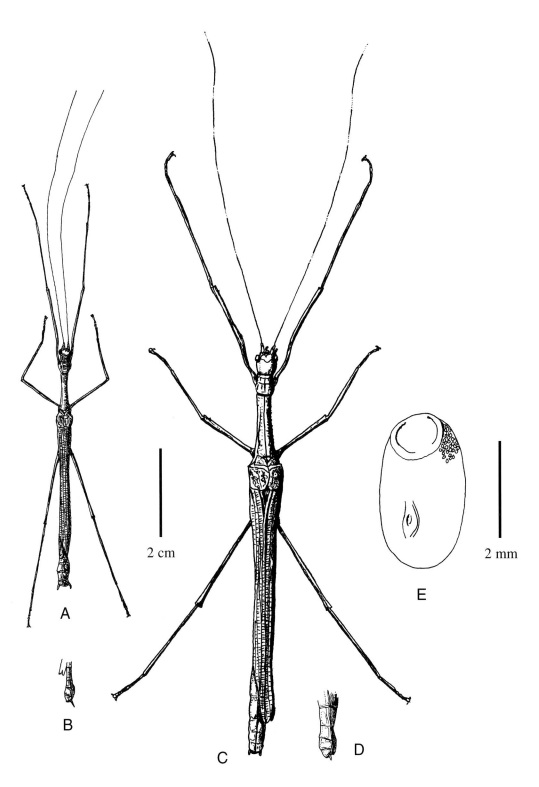

2 cm

2 mm

A

B

C

D

E

Marmessoidea rosea (Fabricius 1793). A & B. Male. C & D. Female. E. Egg.

Plate 56

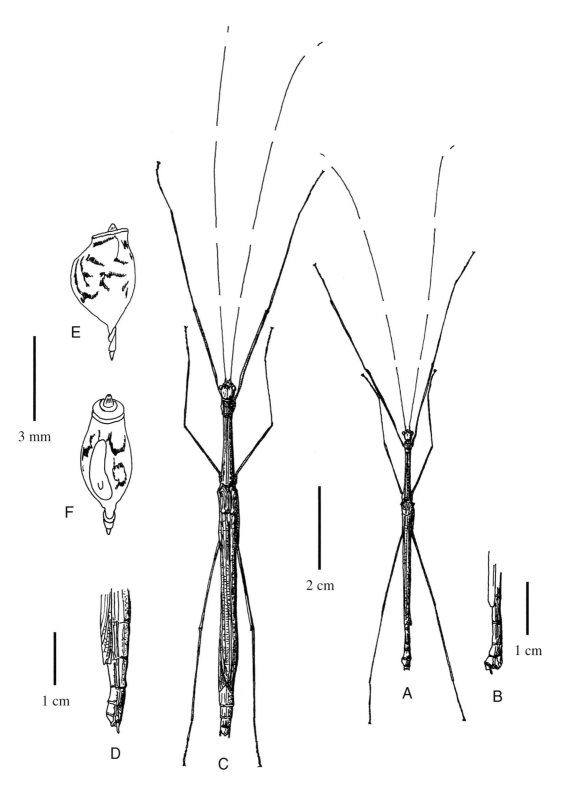

Marmessoidea annulata (Fabricius 1798). A & B. Male. C & D. Female. E & F. Egg.

Plate 57

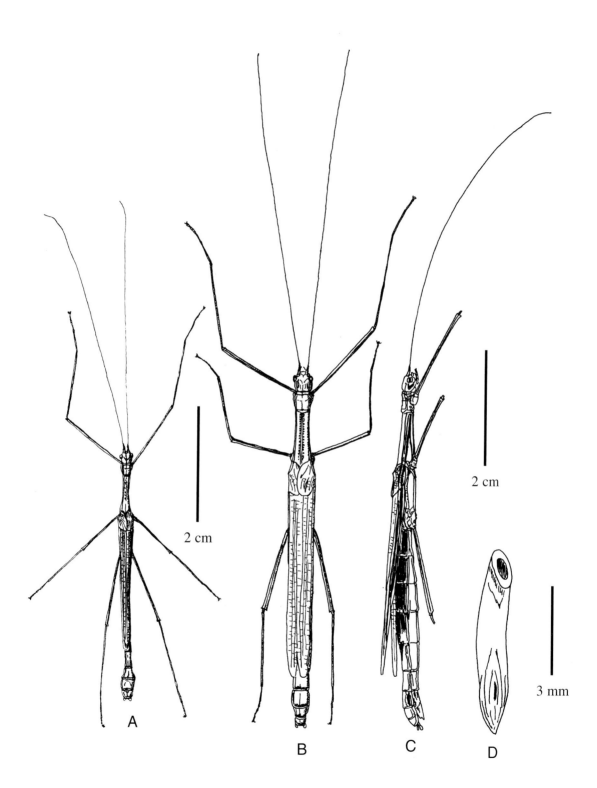

Necroscia marginata (Gray 1835). A. Male. B & C. Female. D. Egg.

Plate 58

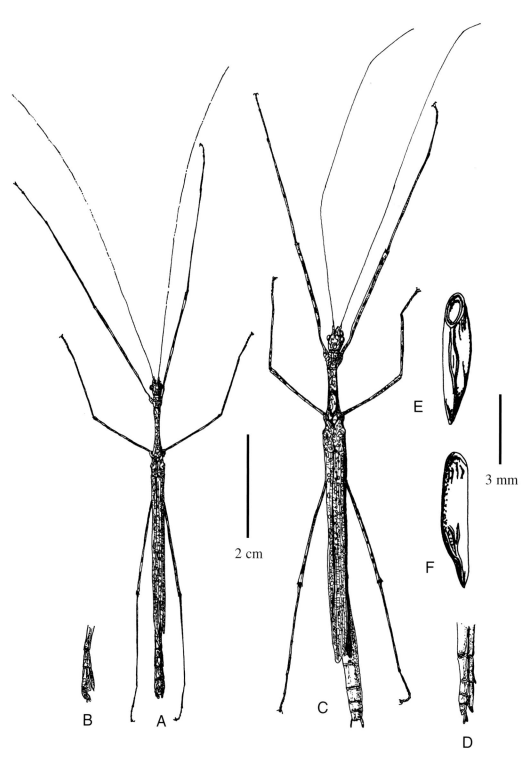

Necroscia punctata (Gray 1835). A & B. Male. C & D. Female. E & F. Egg.

Plate 59

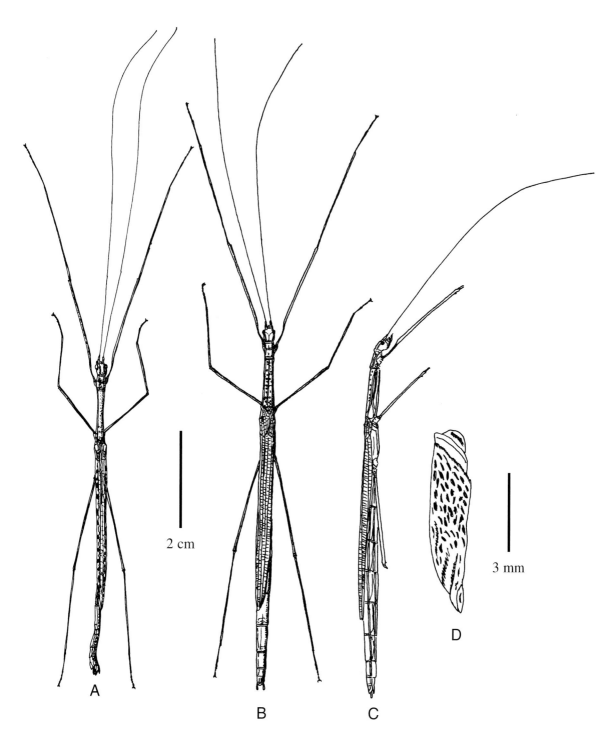

Necroscia affinis (Gray 1835). A. Male. B & C. Female. D. Egg.

Plate 60

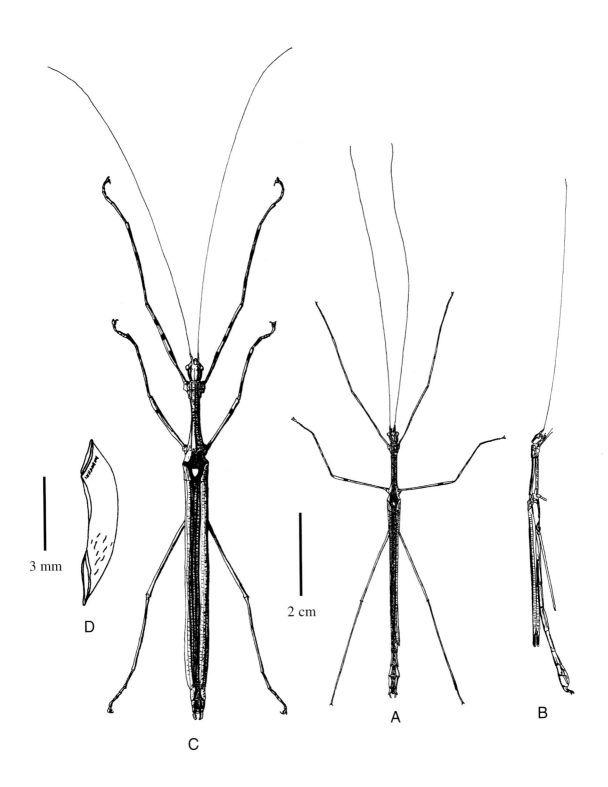

3 mm

D

2 cm

C

A

B

Necroscia annulipes (Gray 1835). A & B. Male. C. Female. D. Egg.

Plate 61

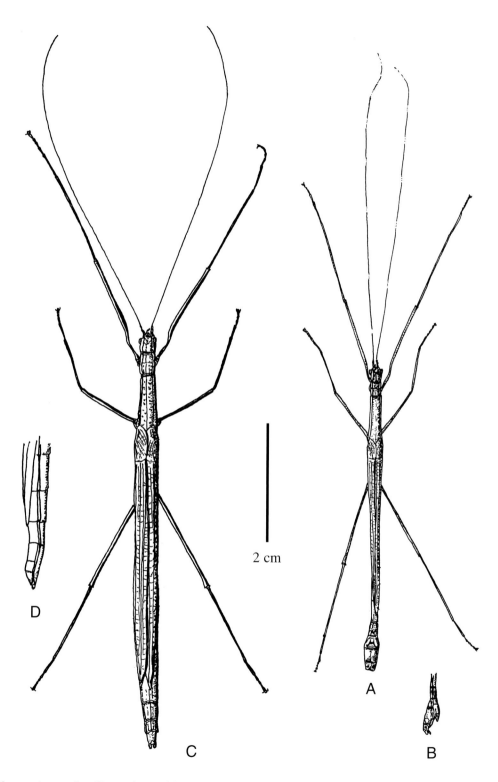

Necroscia prasina (Burmeister 1838). A & B. Male. C & D. Female.

2 cm

Plate 62

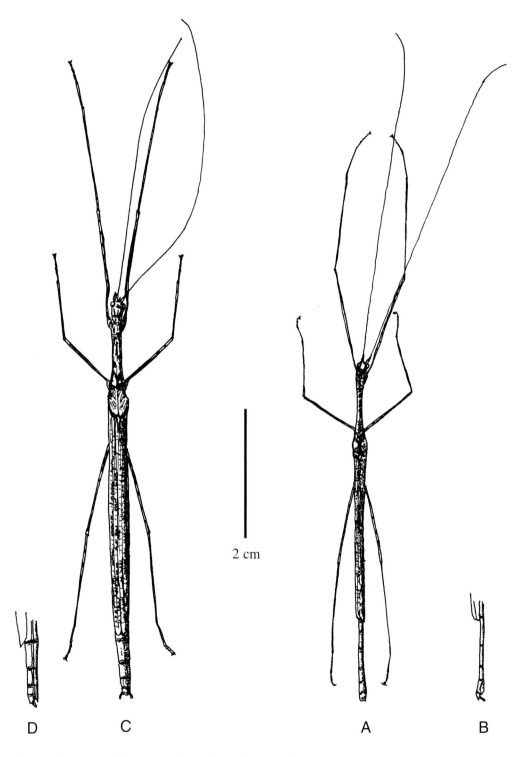

D   C   A   B

2 cm

Necroscia westwoodi Kirby 1904. A & B. Male. C & D. Female.

Plate 63

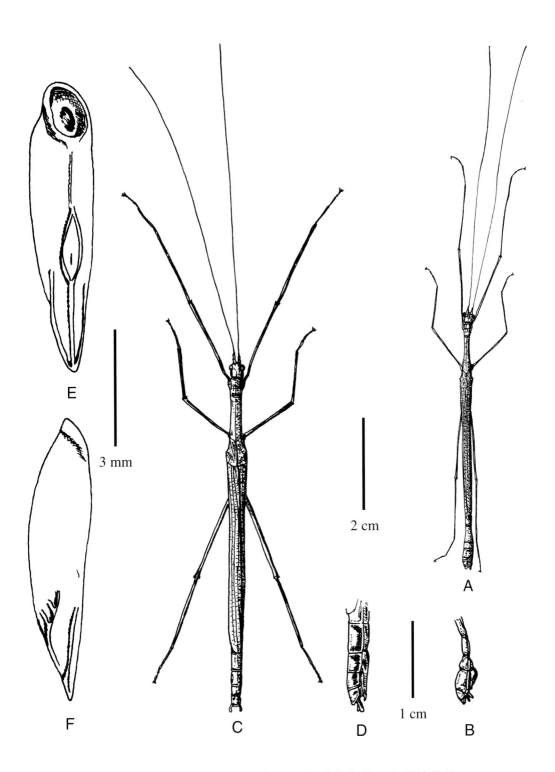

3 mm

2 cm

1 cm

E

F

A

B

C

D

Necroscia inflata (Redtenbacher 1908). A & B. Male. C & D. Female. E & F. Egg.

Plate 64

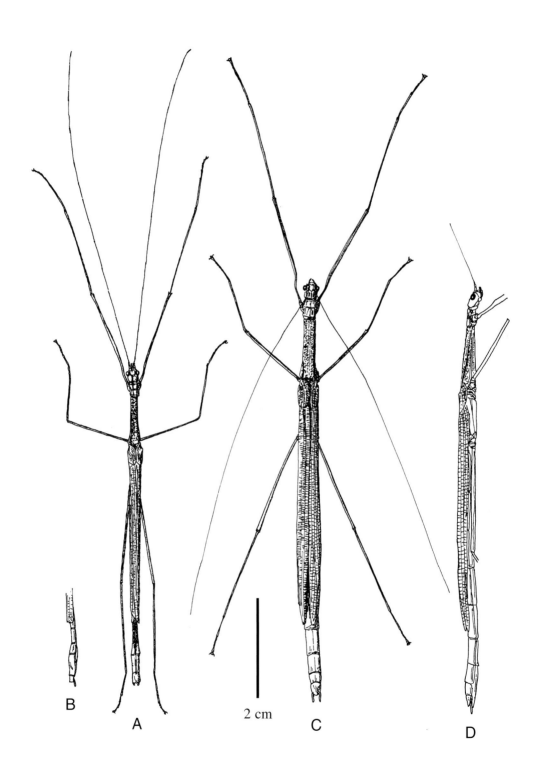

B

A

2 cm

C

D

Necroscia kotatinggia Brock 1998. A & B. Male. C & D. Female.

Plate 65

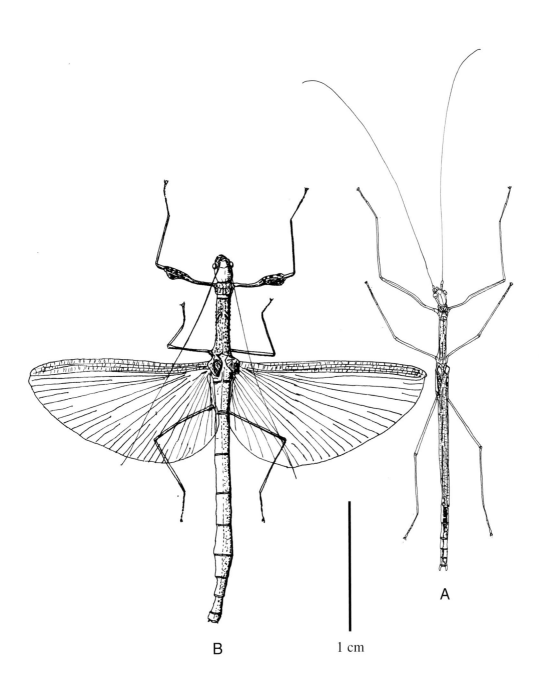

Lobonecroscia subflava Brock & Seow-Choen sp. nov. A. Male. B. Female.

Plate 66

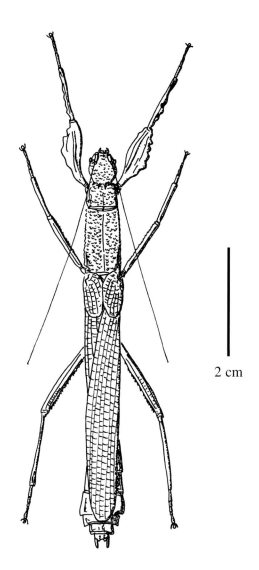

Neoclides magistralis (Redtenbacher 1908). Female.

Plate 67

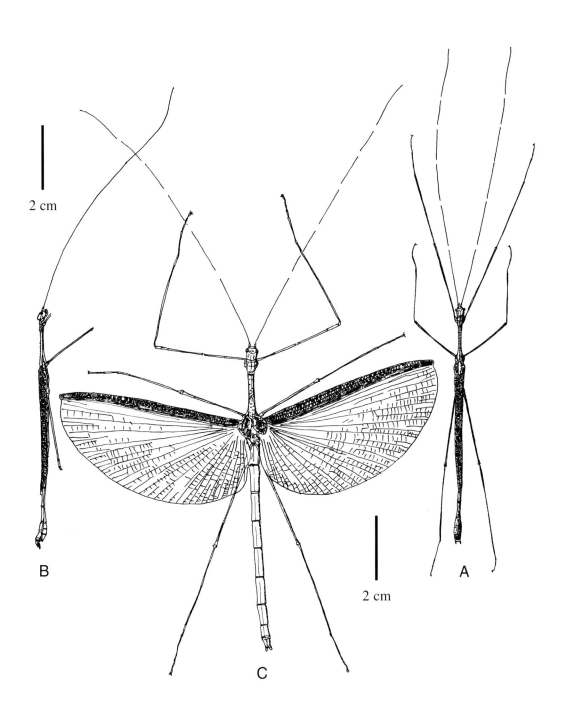

Orthonecroscia filum (Westwood 1848). A & B. Male. C. Female.

Plate 68

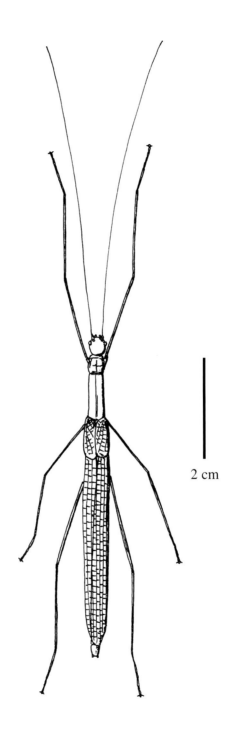

2 cm

Paranecroscia operculata Redtenbacher 1908. Female (after Brock).

Plate 69

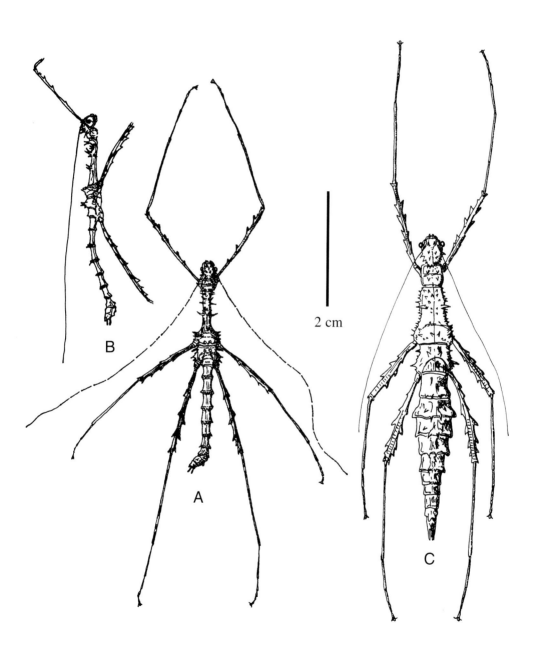

Parasteneboea yehi Brock 1998. A & B. Male. C. Female.

Plate 70

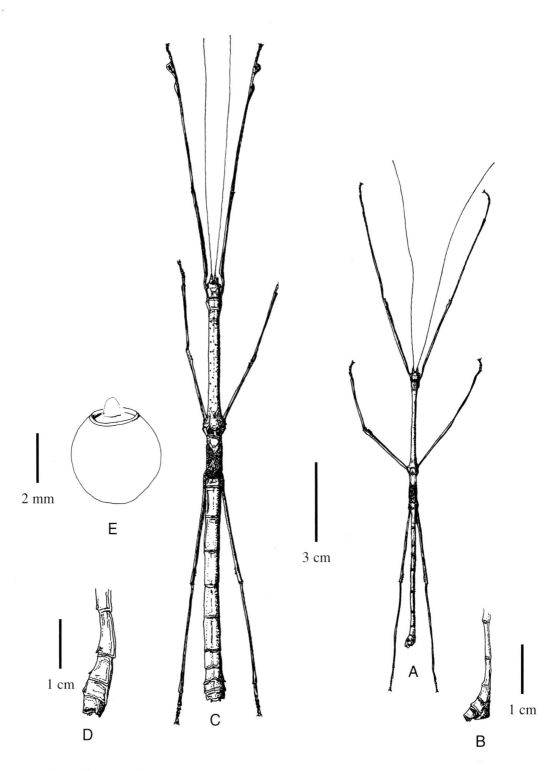

Phaenopharos struthioneus (Westwood 1859). A & B. Male. C & D. Female. E. Egg.

Plate 71

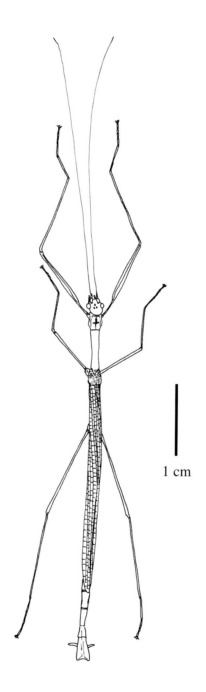

1 cm

Scionecra microptera (Redtenbacher 1908). Male.

Plate 72

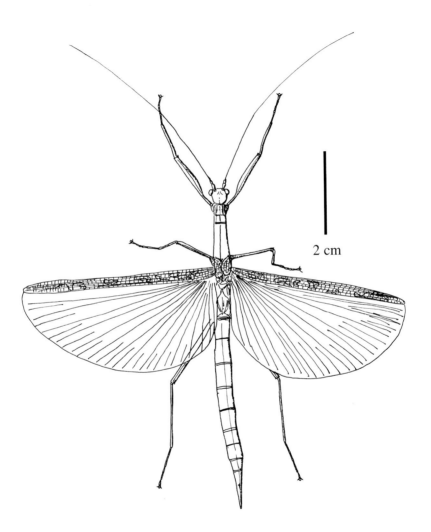

2 cm

Sipyloidea sordida (de Haan 1842). Female.

Plate 73

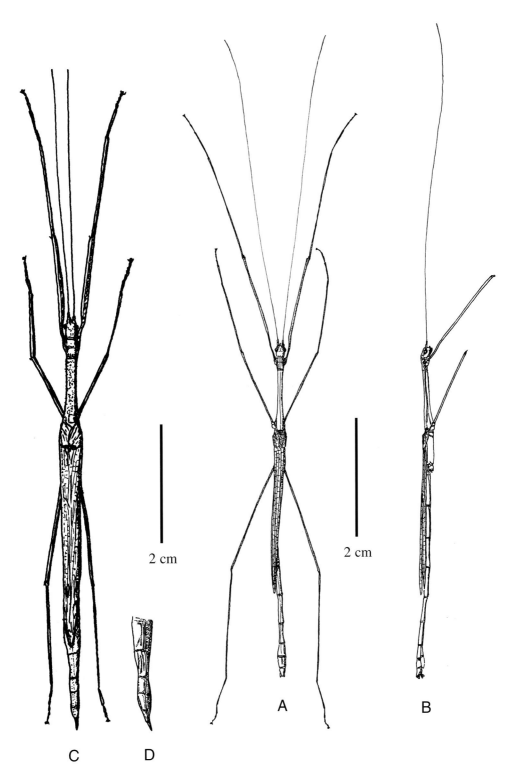

2 cm

2 cm

A

B

C   D

Sipyloidea sipylus (Westwood 1859). A & B. Male. C & D. Female.

Plate 74

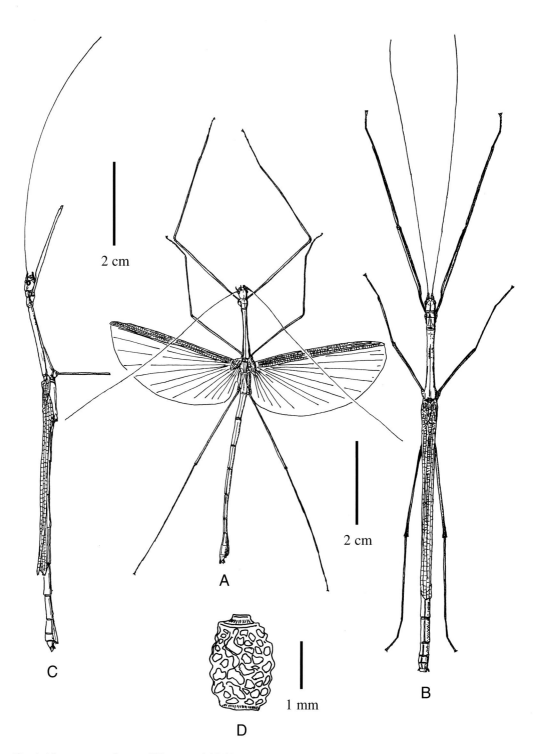

Sipyloidea meneptolemus (Westwood 1859). A. Male. B & C. Female. D. Egg.

Plate 75

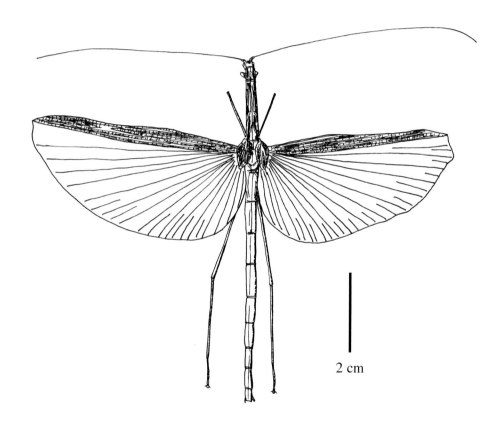

Sipyloidea magna Redtenbacher 1908 (Holotype). Female.

2 cm

Plate 76

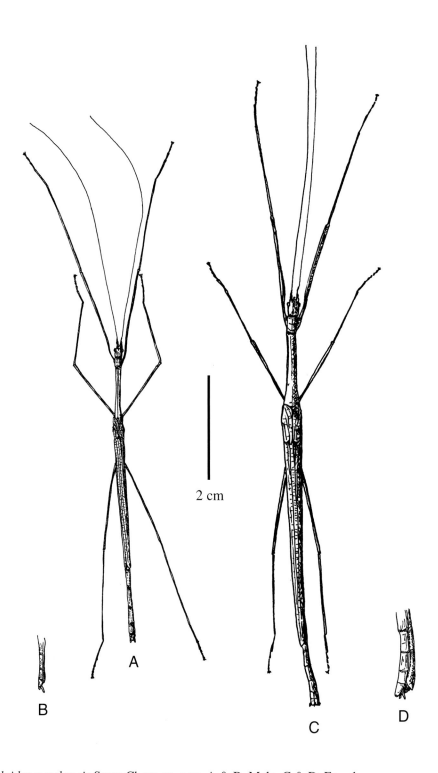

Sipyloidea perakensis Seow-Choen sp. nov. A & B. Male. C & D. Female.

Plate 77

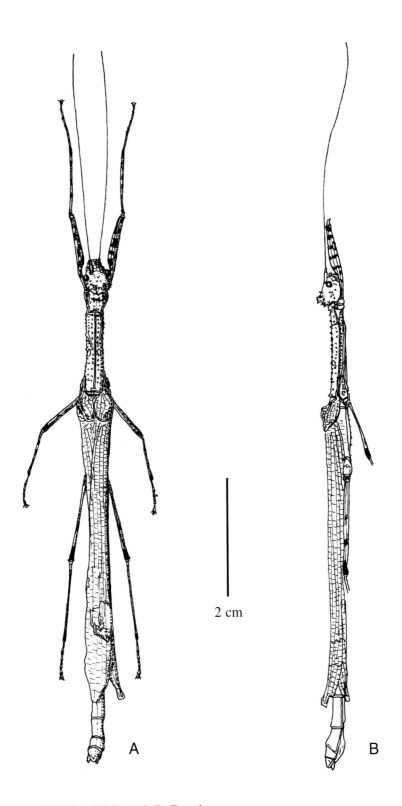

Sosibia aurita (Fabricius 1793). A & B. Female.

Plate 78

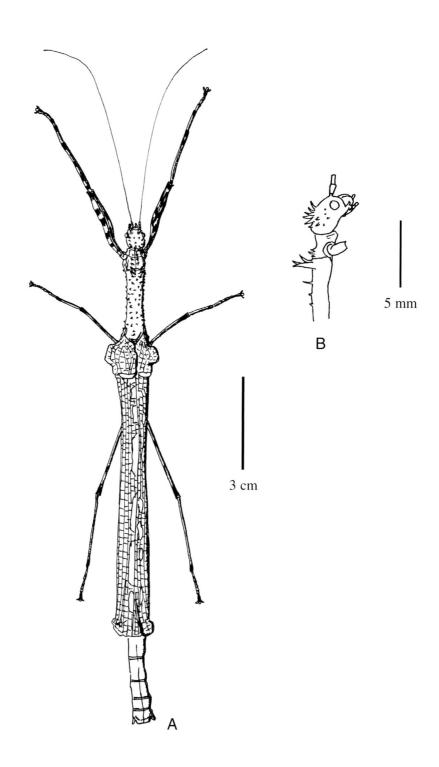

5 mm

3 cm

B

A

Sosibia curtipes (Westwood 1848). A. Female. B. Side view of the head of a male.

Plate 79

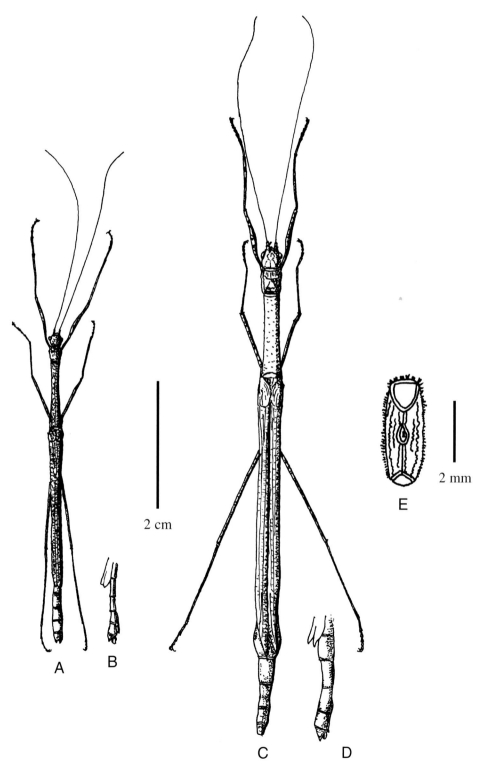

2 cm

2 mm

A   B

C   D

E

Sosibia esacus (Westwood 1859). A & B. Male. C & D. Female. E. Egg.

Plate 80

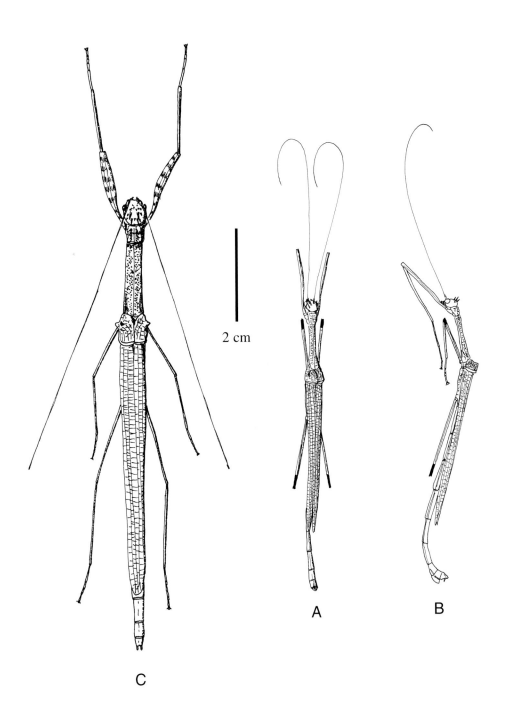

2 cm

A

B

C

Sosibia nigrispina Stål 1875. A & B. Male. C. Female (after Brock).

Plate 81

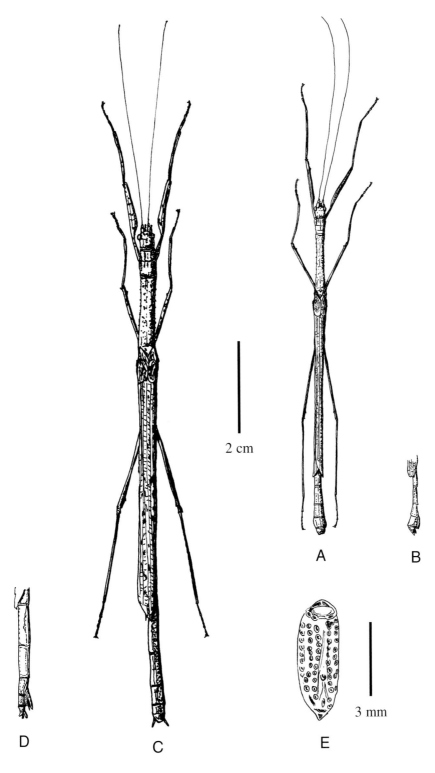

A

B

D

C

E

2 cm

3 mm

Sosibia solida Redtenbacher 1908. A & B. Male. C & D. Female. E. Egg.

Plate 82

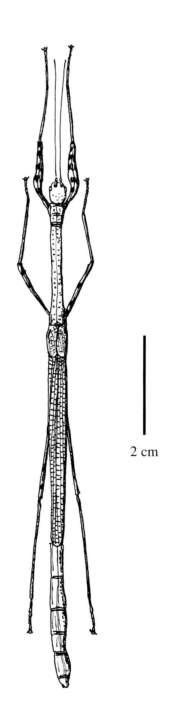

2 cm

Sosibia macera Redtenbacher 1908. Female.

Plate 83

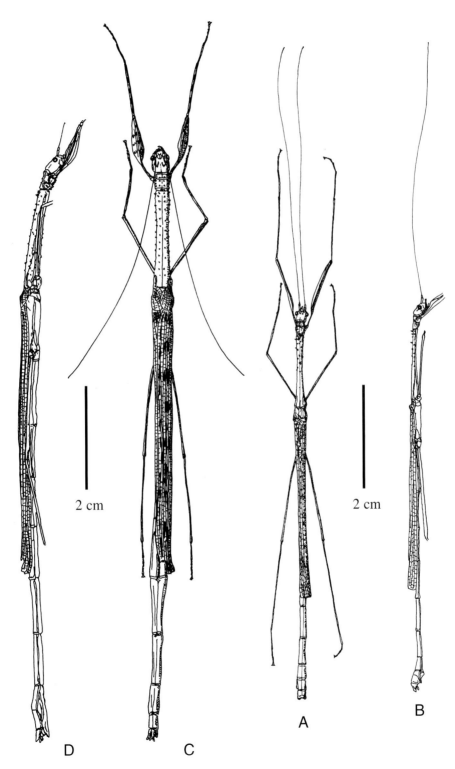

2 cm

2 cm

D   C   A

B

Sosibia brocki Seow-Choen sp. nov. A & B. Male. C & D. Female.

Plate 84

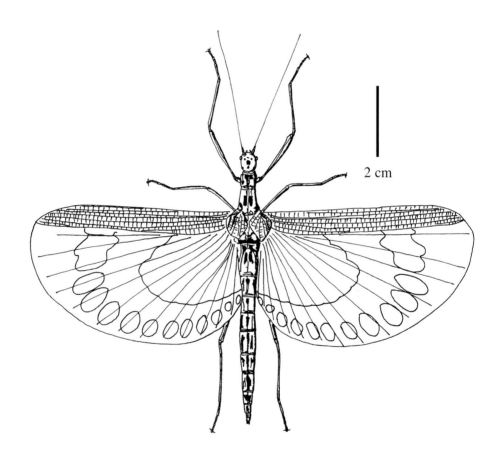

2 cm

Tagesoidea tages (Westwood 1859). Female.

Plate 85

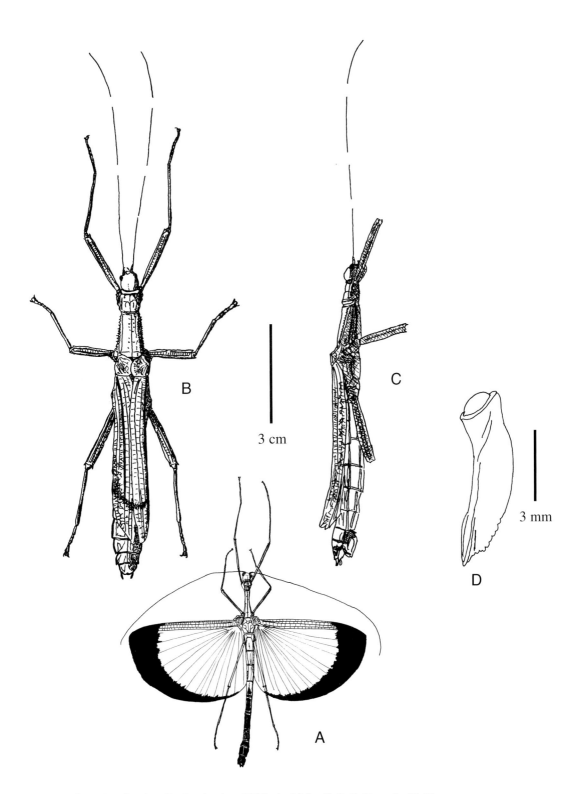

Tagesoidea nigrofasciata Redtenbacher 1908. A. Male. B & C. Female. D. Egg.

Plate 86

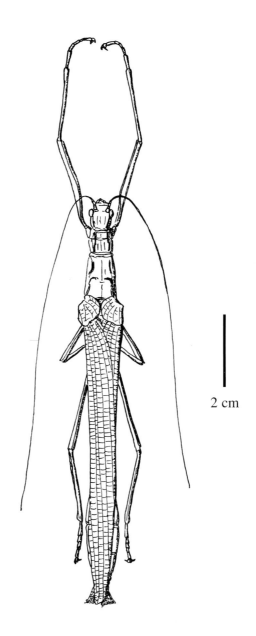

2 cm

Trachythorax atrosignatus (Brunner 1893). Female.

Plate 87

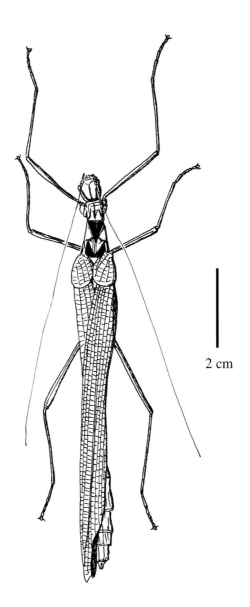

2 cm

Trachythorax gohi Brock 1999. Female.

Plate 88

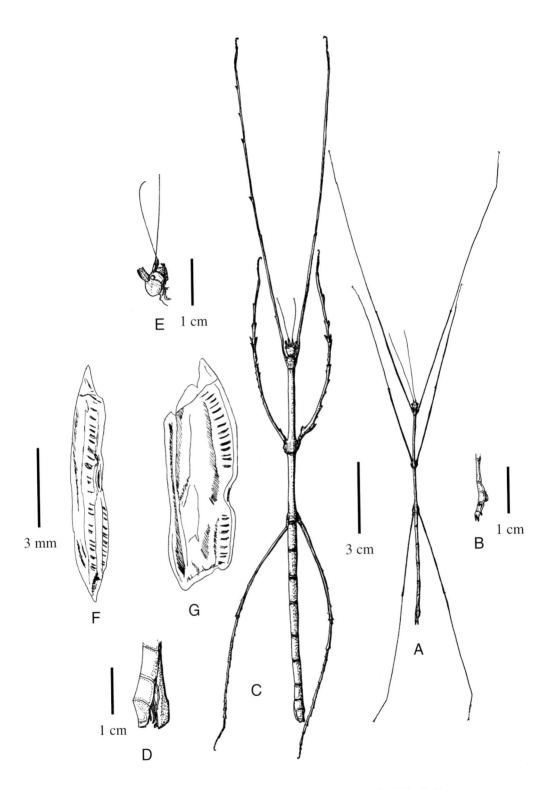

Baculum nematodes (de Haan 1842). A & B. Male. C–E. Female. F & G. Egg.

Plate 89

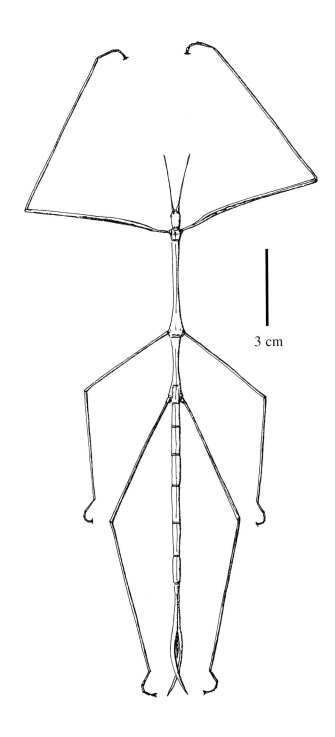

3 cm

Erringtonia malaccensis Brunner 1907. Female. (after Brunner).

Plate 90

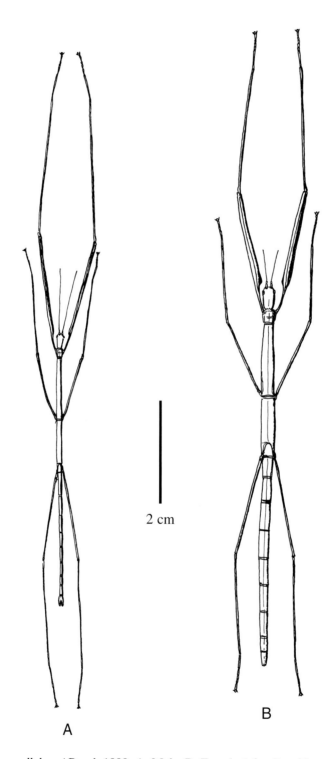

A

B

Parabaculum pendleburyi Brock 1999. A. Male. B. Female (after Brock).

Plate 91

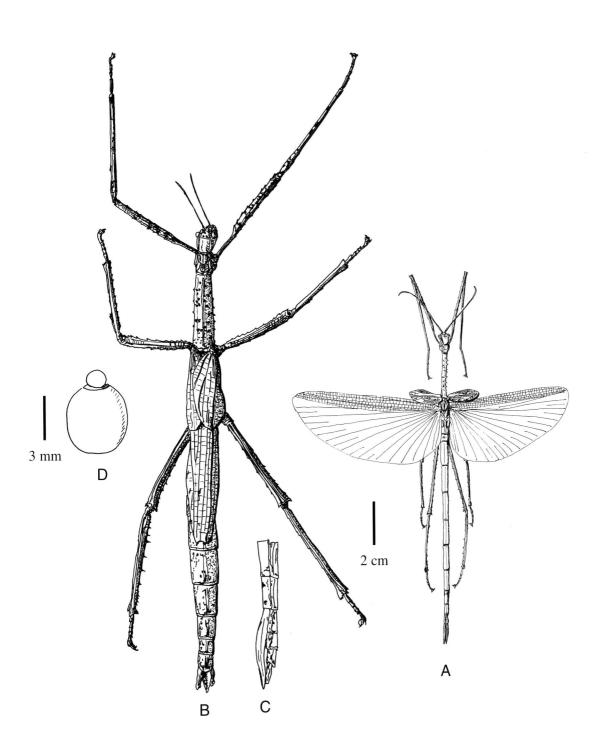

Eurycnema versirubra (Audinet-Serville 1838). A. Male. B & C. Female. D. Egg.

Plate 92

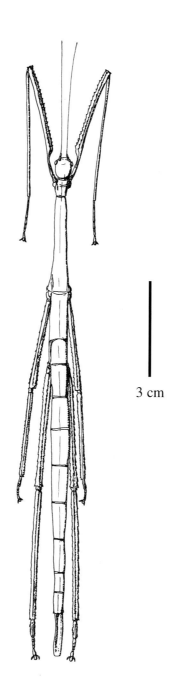

3 cm

Nearchus grubaueri Redtenbacher 1908. Female.

Plate 93

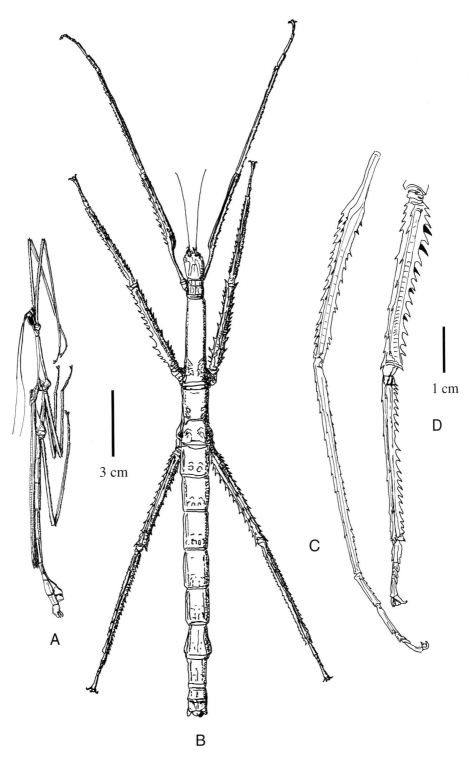

A

B

C

D

3 cm

1 cm

Pharnacia sumatranus (Brunner von Wattenwyl 1907). A. Male. B. Female. C. Left fore leg.
D. Left mid leg.

Plate 94

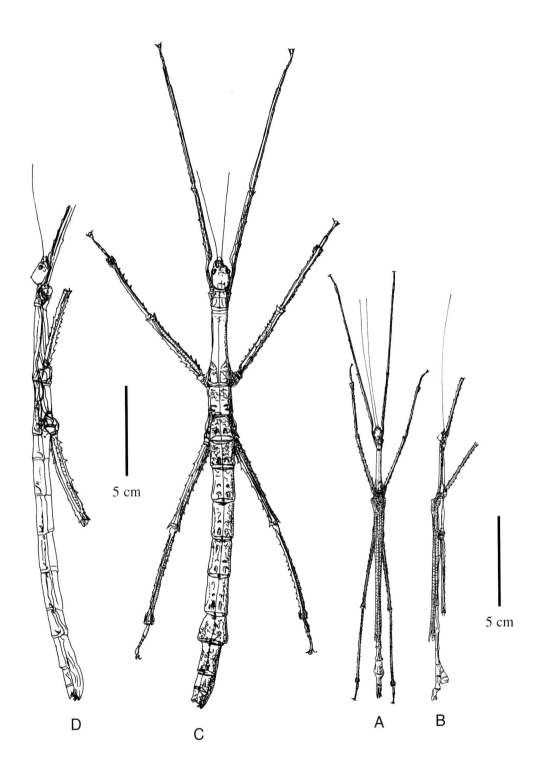

5 cm

5 cm

D

C

A

B

Pharnacia cantori (Westwood 1859). A & b. Male. C & D. Female.

Plate 95

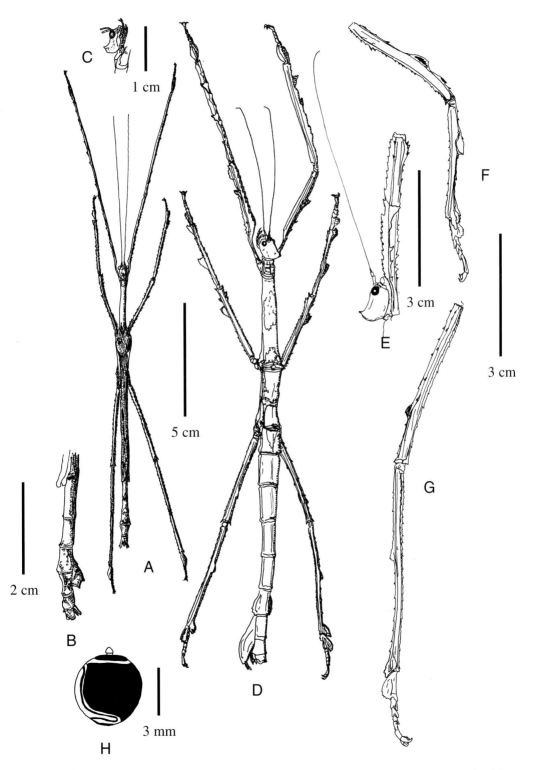

Pharnacia cantori (Westwood 1859). A–C. Male. D & E. Female. F. Left fore leg. G. Left mid leg. H. Egg.

Plate 96

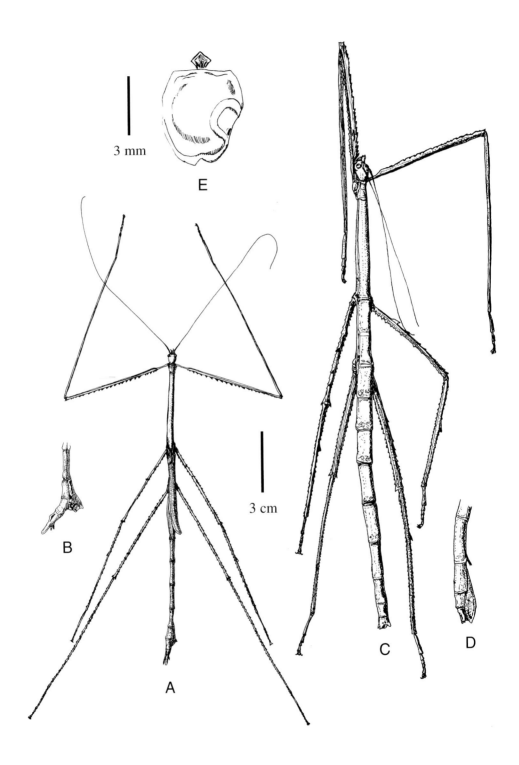

3 mm

E

3 cm

B

A

C

D

Phobaeticus serratipes (Gray 1835). A & B. Male. C & D Female. E. Egg.

Plate 97

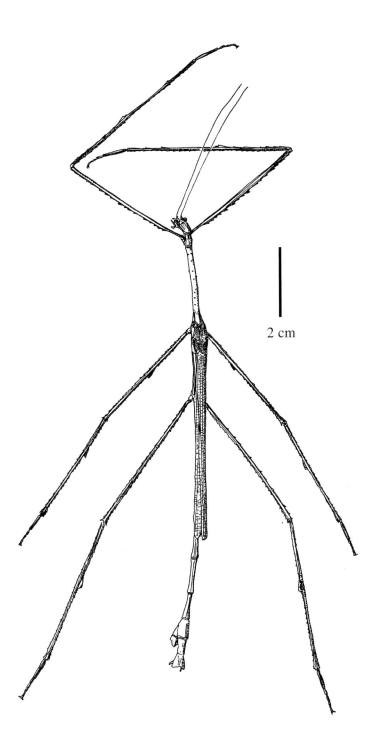

2 cm

Phobaeticus tirachus (Westwood 1859). Male.

Plate 98

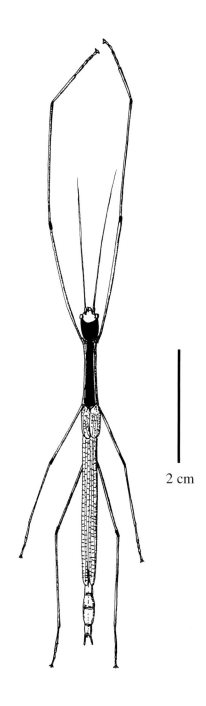

2 cm

Ophicrania flavomaculata Brock 1999. Female. (after Brock).

Plate 99

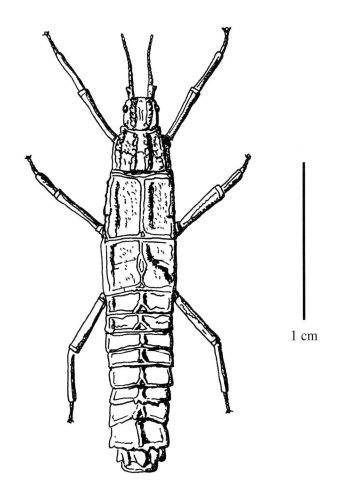

1 cm

Planispectrum bengalensis (Redtenbacher 1906). Female.

Plate 100

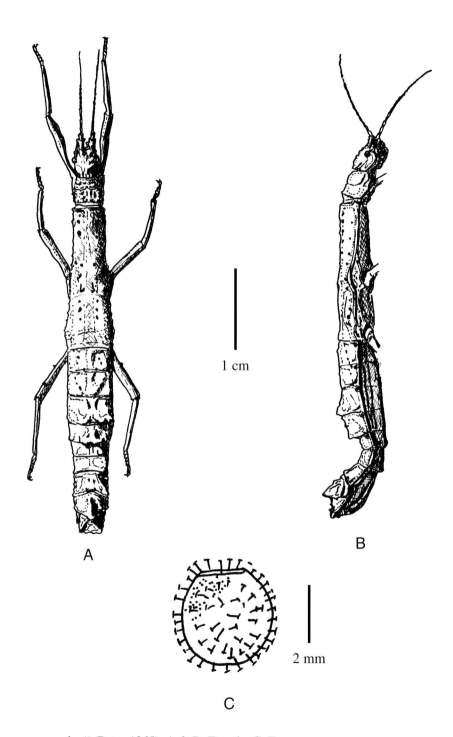

Pylaemenes mouhotii (Bates 1865). A & B. Female. C. Egg.

Plate 101

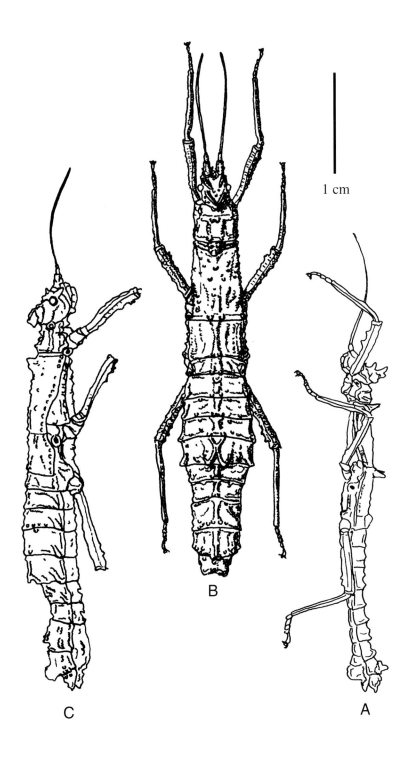

1 cm

B

C

A

Pylaemenes oileus (Westwood 1859), Java. A. Male. B & C. Female.

Plate 102

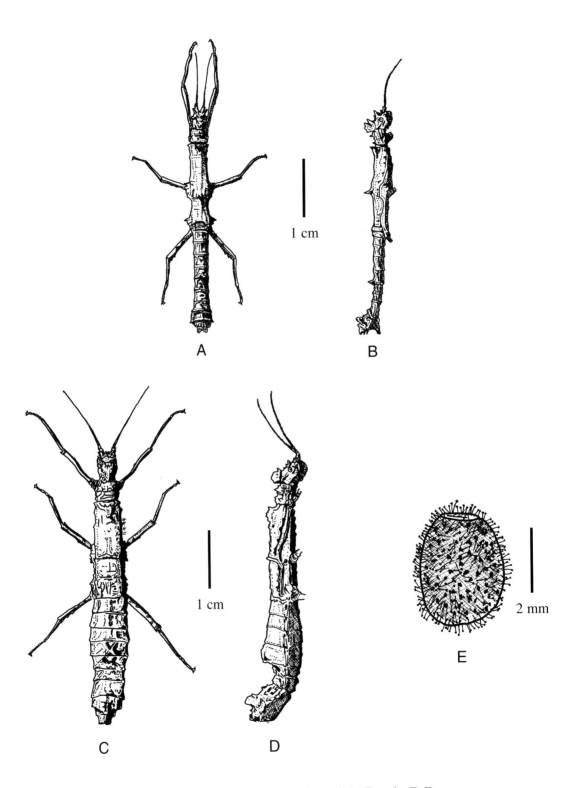

Pylaemenes mitratus Redtenbacher 1906. A & B. Male. C & D. Female. E. Egg.

Plate 103

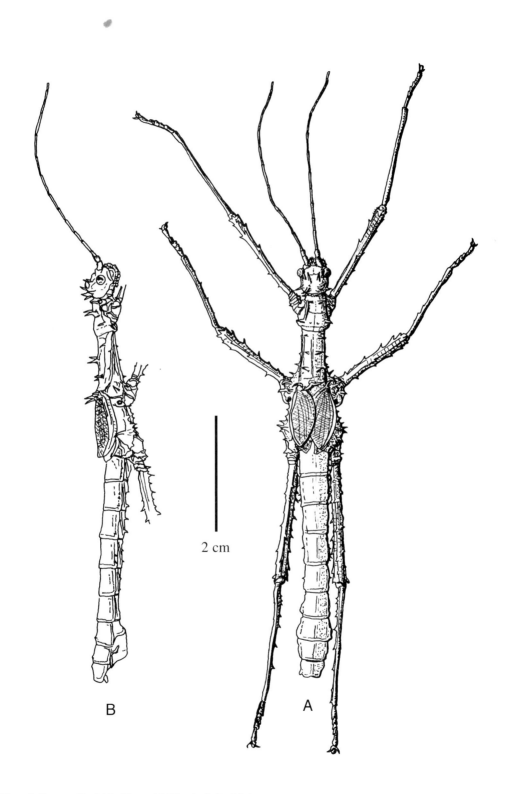

2 cm

B

A

Haaniella muelleri (de Haan 1842). A & B. Male.

Plate 104

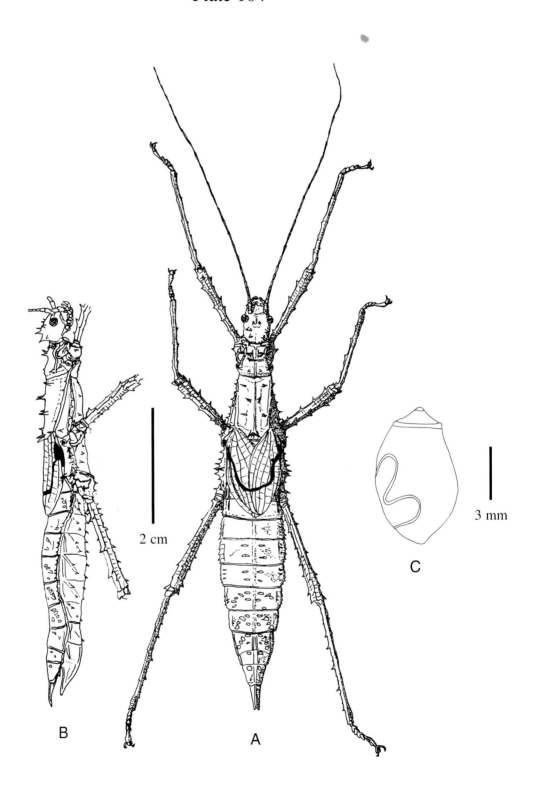

Haaniella muelleri (de Haan 1842). A & B. Female. C. Egg

Plate 105

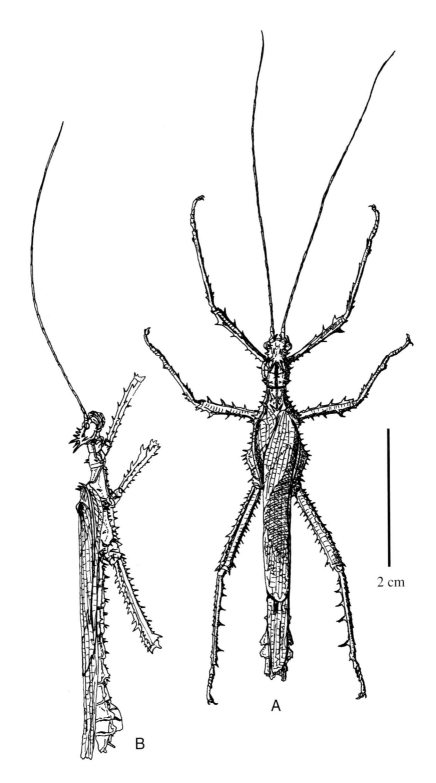

Heteropteryx dilatata (Parkinson 1798). A & B. Male.

Plate 106

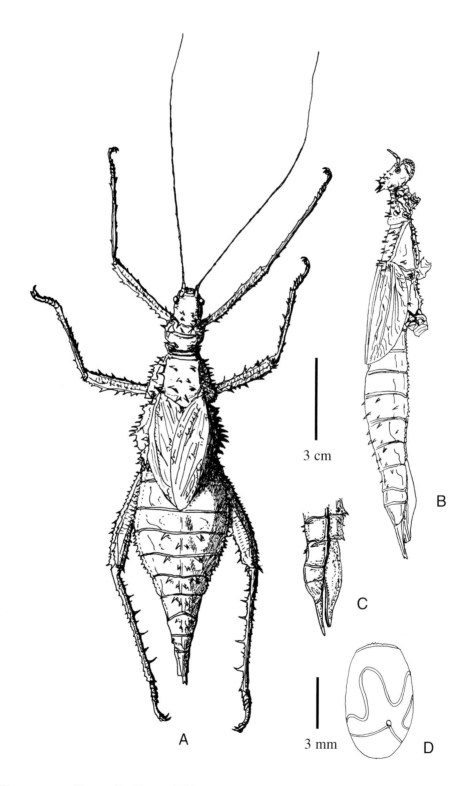

3 cm

3 mm

A

B

C

D

Heteropteryx dilatata (Parkinson 1798). A–C. Female. D. Egg.

Plate 107

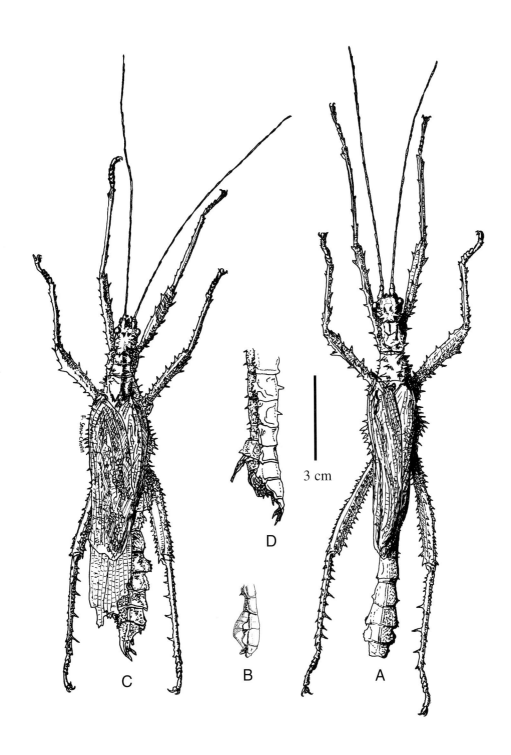

3 cm

Heteropteryx dilatata (Parkinson 1798). A–D. Gynandromorphs.

Plate 108

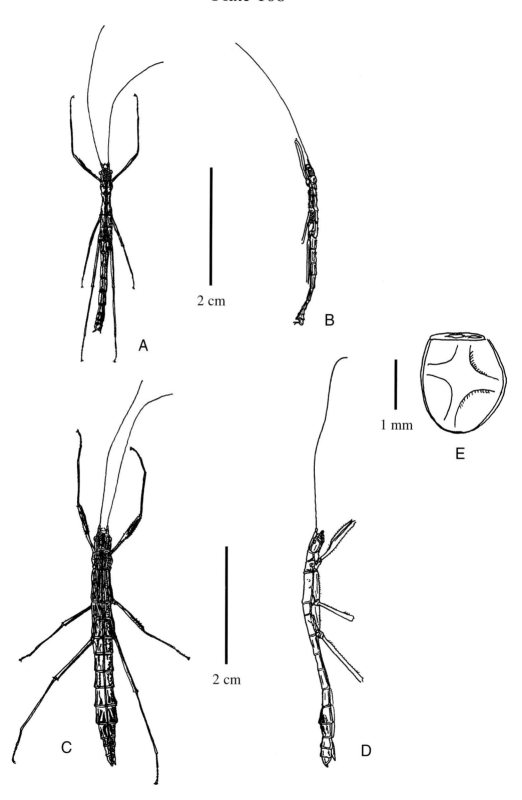

2 cm

A

B

2 cm

C

D

1 mm

E

Abrosoma festinatum Brock & Seow-Choen 1995. A & B. Male. C & D. Female. E. Egg.

Plate 109

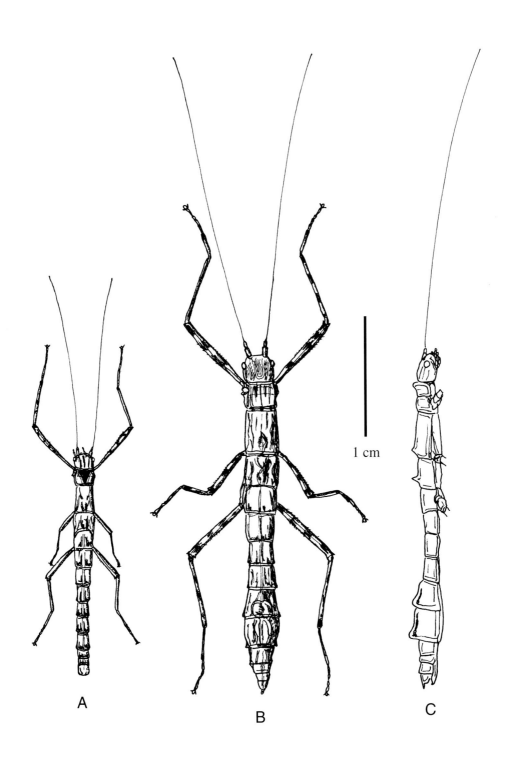

Abrosoma gibberum Brock & Seow-Choen 1995. A. Male. B & C. Female.

Plate 110

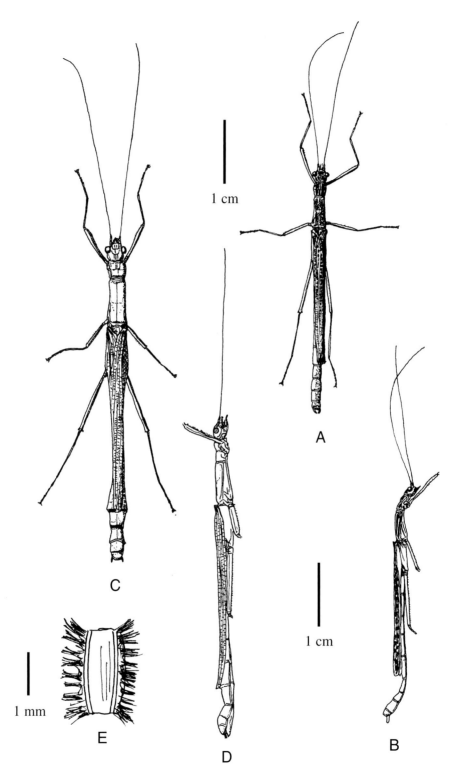

1 cm

1 cm

1 mm

A

B

C

D

E

Abrosoma xiuyuae Brock & Seow-Choen 1999. A & B. Male. C & D. Female. E. Egg.

Plate 111

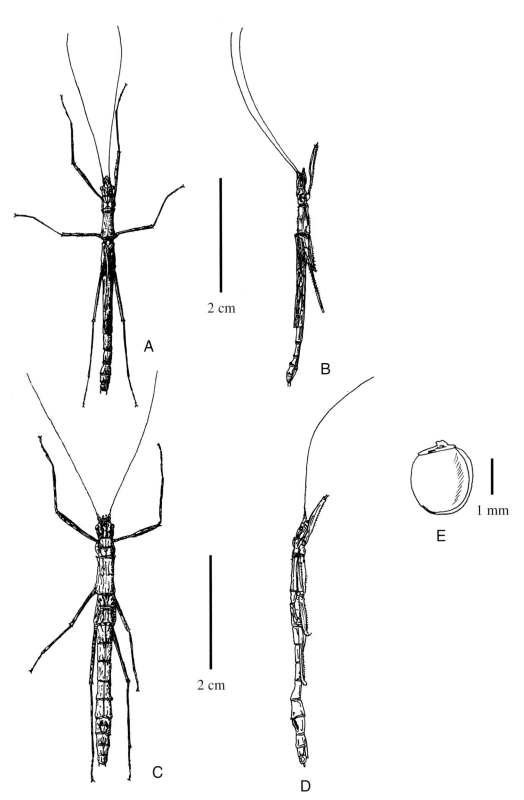

2 cm

A

B

2 cm

C

D

1 mm

E

Abrosoma johorensis Seow-Choen & Goh 1999. A & B. Male. C & D. Female. E. Egg.

Plate 112

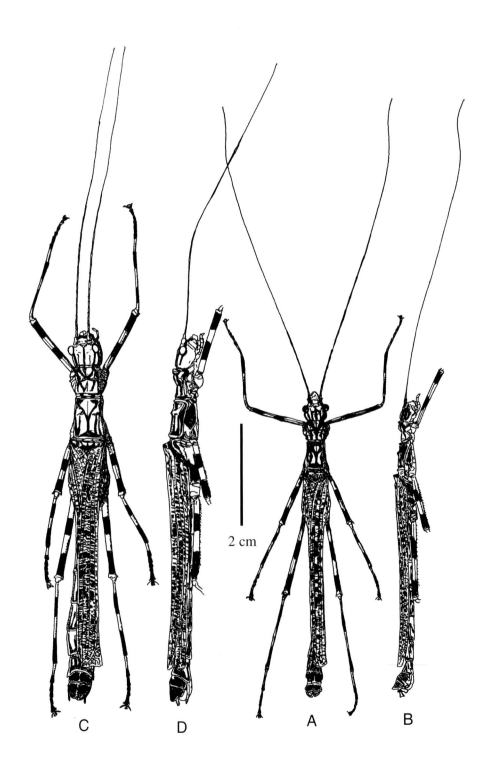

2 cm

C   D   A   B

Aschiphasma annulipes Westwood 1830. A & B. Male. C & D. Female.

Plate 113

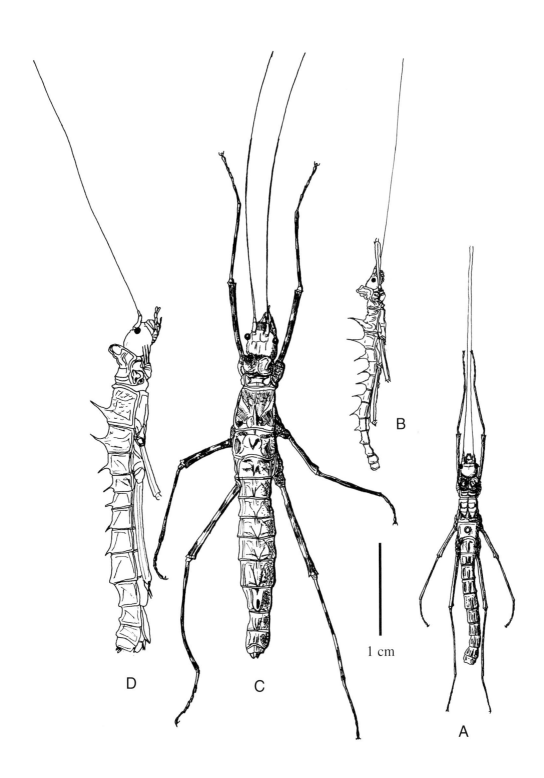

Pinnispinus harmani Brock 1995. A & B. Male. C & D. Female.

Plate 114

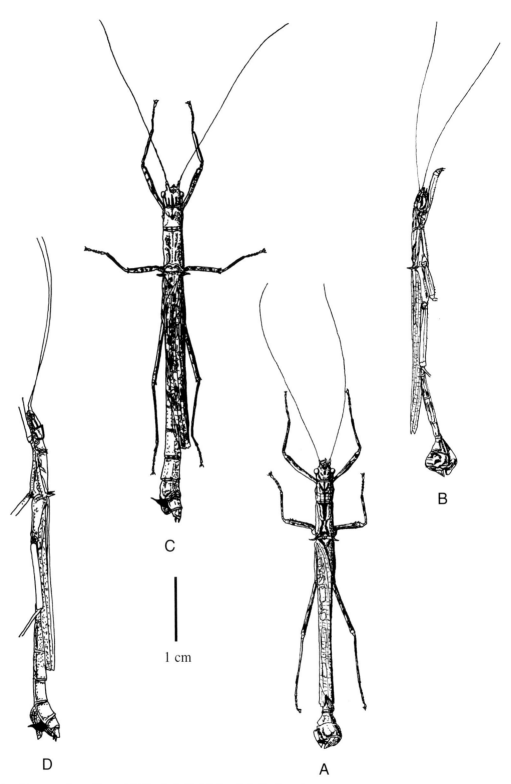

C

B

1 cm

D

A

Presbistus peleus (Gray 1835). A & B. Male. C & D. female.

Plate 115

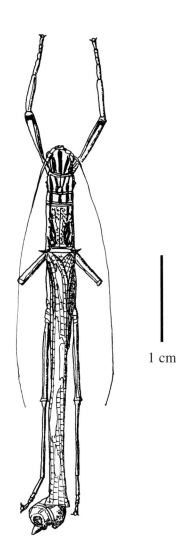

1 cm

Presbistus flavicornis (de Haan 1842). Male.

Plate 116

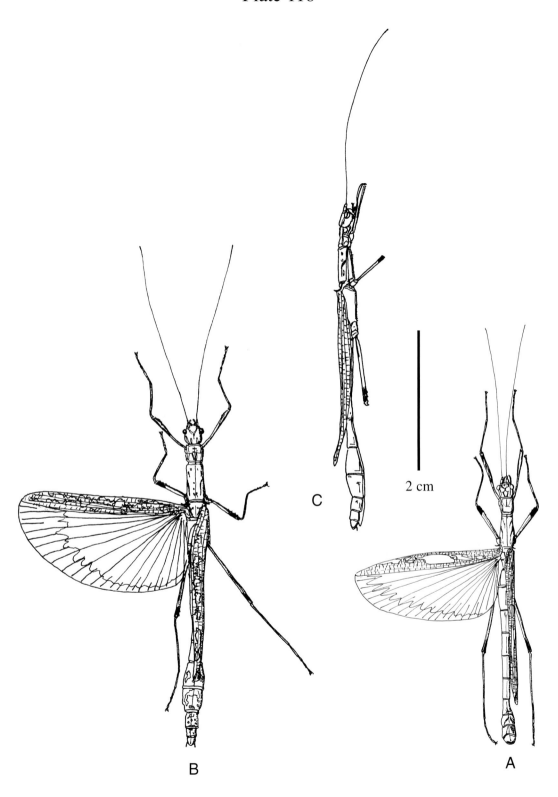

2 cm

C

B

A

Presbistus horni (Redtenbacher 1908). A. Male. B & C. Female.

Plate 117

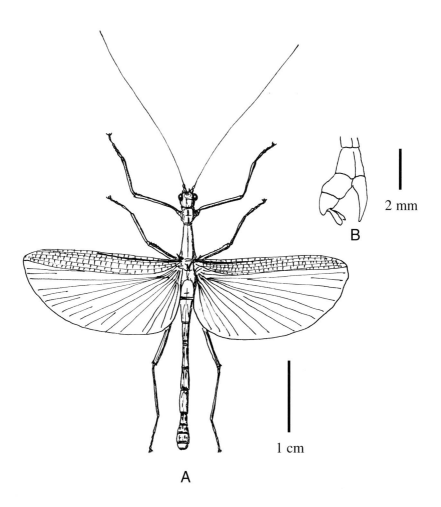

2 mm

B

1 cm

A

Presbistus eryx (Westwood 1859). A. Male.

Plate 118

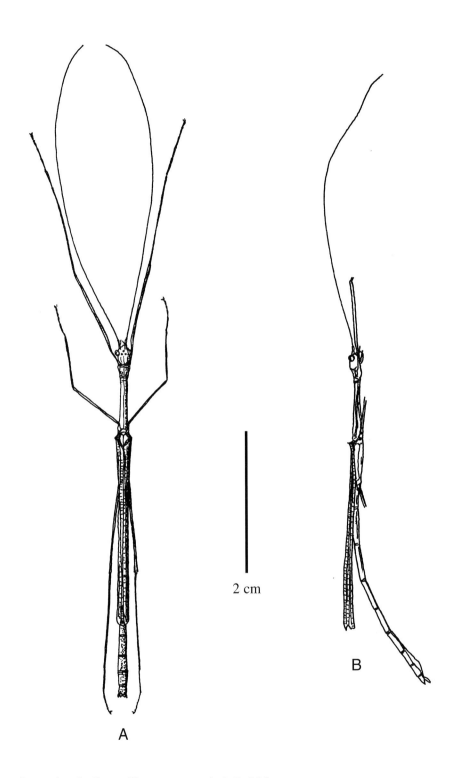

2 cm

A

B

Presbistus fragilis Seow-Choen sp. nov. A & B. Male

Plate 119

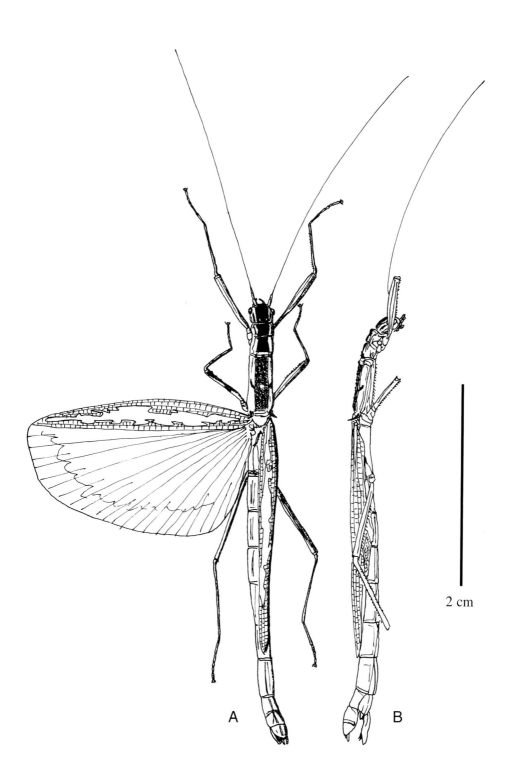

2 cm

Presbistus sp. 1 (unidentified). A & B. Female.

Plate 120

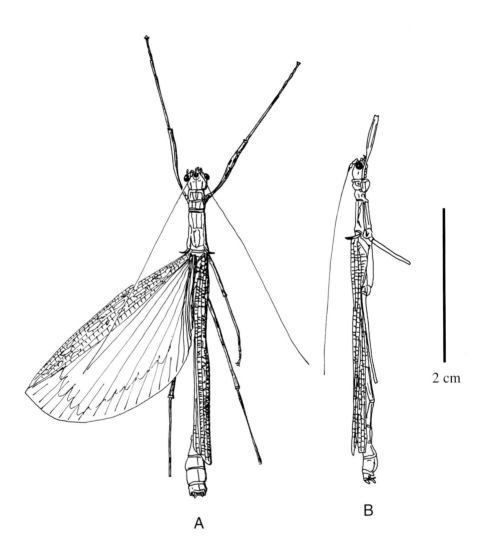

2 cm

A

B

Presbistus sp. 2 (unidentified). A & B. Female.

Plate 121

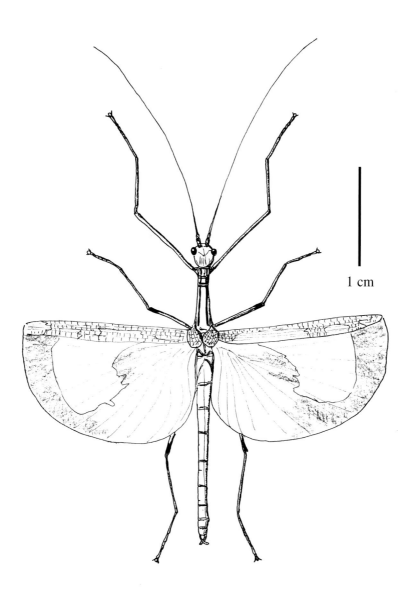

1 cm

Kalocorinnis pulchella (de Haan 1842). Male.

Plate 122

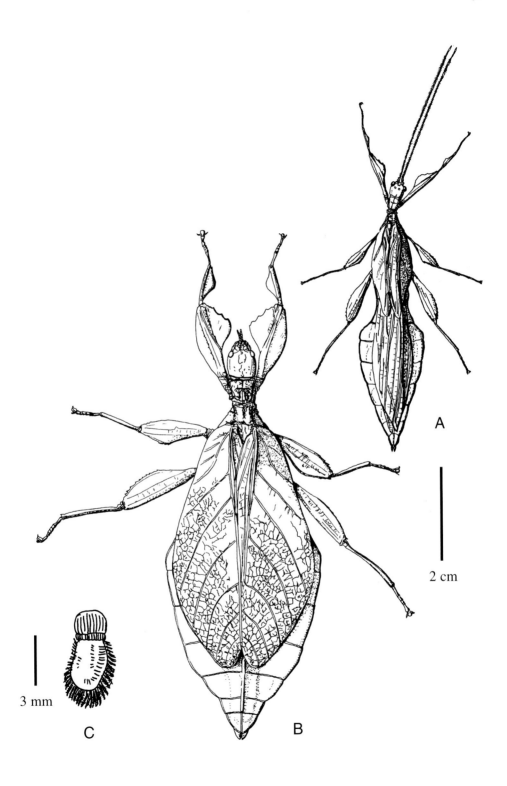

Phyllium siccifolium (Linnaeus 1758). A. Male. B. Female. C. Egg.

Plate 123

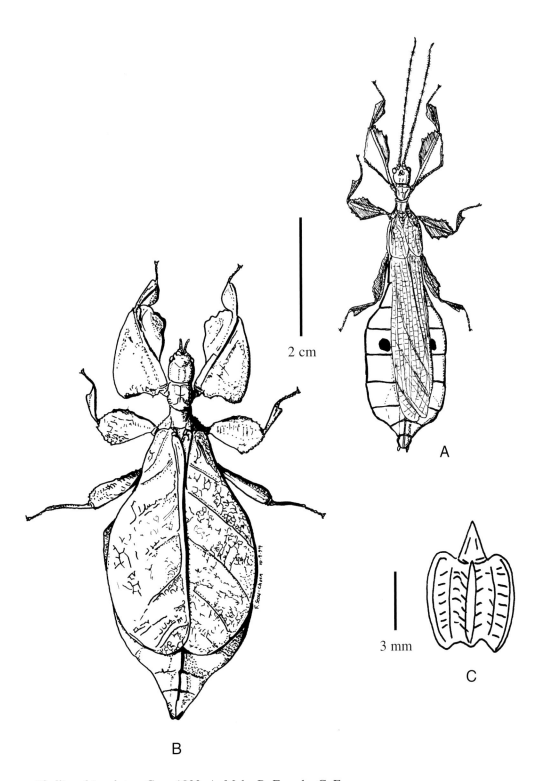

2 cm

A

3 mm

C

B

Phyllium bioculatum Gray 1832. A. Male. B. Female. C. Egg.

Plate 124

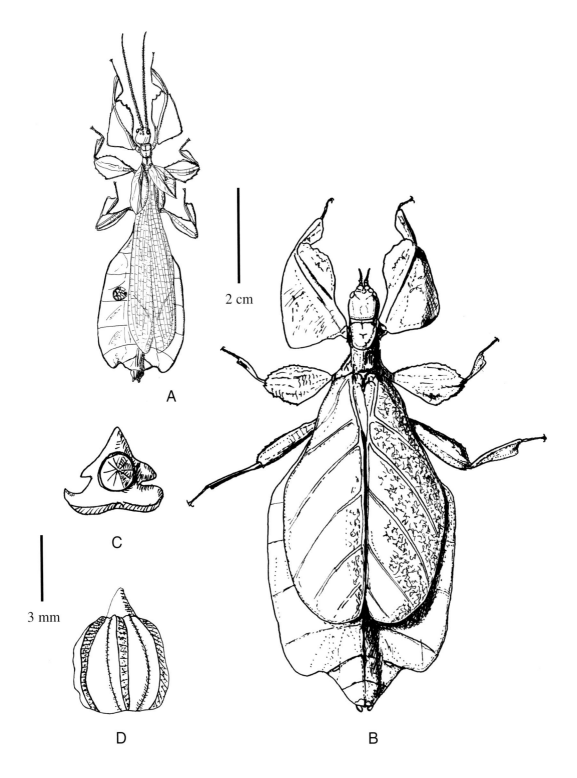

2 cm

3 mm

A

C

D

B

Phyllium pulchrifolium Audinet-serville 1838. A. Male. B. Female. C & D. Egg.

Plate 125

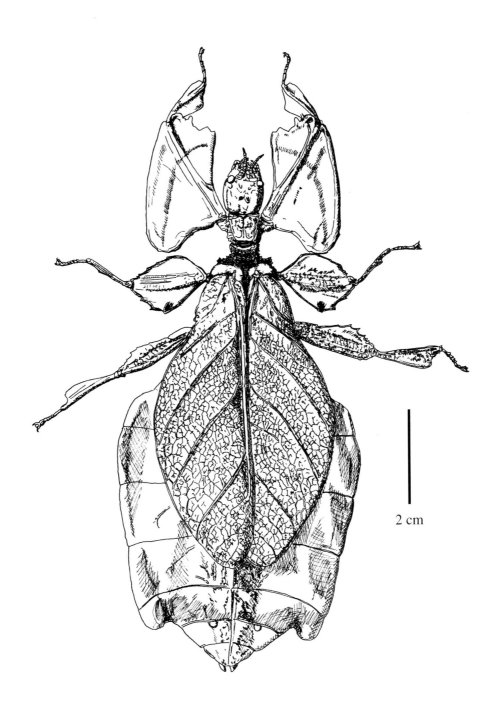

2 cm

Phyllium giganteum Hausleithner 1984. Female.

Plate 126

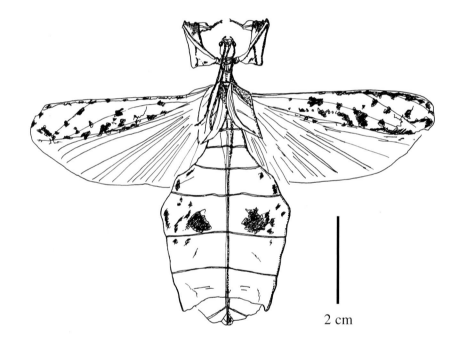

2 cm

Phyllium giganteum Hausleithner 1984. Male.

Plate 127

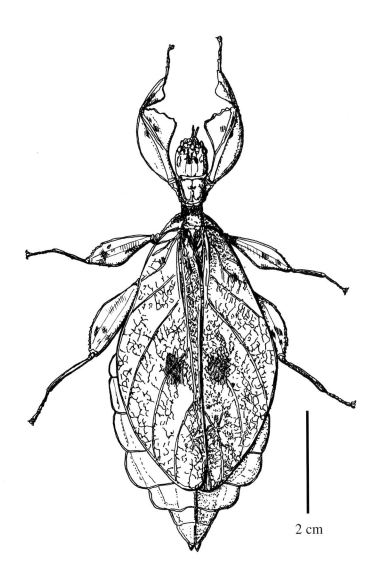

2 cm

Phyllium hausleithneri Brock 1999. Female.

REFERENCES

Audinet-Serville, J.G. (1838). *Histoire Naturelles des Insects. Orthopteres.* Librarie Encyclopedique de Roret, Paris 18.

Bates, H.W. (1865). Description of fifty two new species of Phasmidae from the collection of Mr W Wilson Saunders, with remarks on the family. *Trans. Linn. Soc. Lond.* 25: 321–59.

Bradley, J.C. & Galil, B.S. (1977). The taxonomic arrangement of the Phasmatodea, with keys to the subfamilies and tribes. *Proc. Entomol. Soc. Wash.* 79: 176–208.

Bragg, P.E. (1993). New synonyms and new records of phasmids (Insecta: Phasmida) in Borneo. *Raffles Bull. Zool.* 41: 31–46.

Brock, P.D. (1981). The Malaysian red winged stick insect—a few notes. *AES Exotic Entomol. Group* 3: 104–6.

——————— (1989). Gynandromorph of the stick insect *Heteropteryx dilatata*. *Bull. Am. Ent. Soc.* 48: 207–11.

——————— (1990). Stick insect hunting in Malaysia. *The Phasmid Study Group Newsletter* 45: 12–4.

——————— (1992). Rearing and studying stick and leaf-insects. *The Amateur Entomologists.* Vol. 22. Feltham.

——————— (1994a). A halved gynandromorph of the stick insect *Heteropteryx dilatata*. *Bull. Am. Ent. Soc.* 53: 33.

——————— (1994b). Notes on the giant leaf-insect. *Phyllium giganteum* Hausleithner (Insecta: Phasmida: Phylliidae) with a description of the newly discovered male. *Malay. Nat. Journ.* 48: 53–7.

——————— (1995a). Catalogue of Stick and Leaf-Insects (Insecta: Phasmida) associated with Peninsular Malaysia and Singapore. *Malay. Nat. Journ.* 49: 83–102.

——————— (1995b). A remarkable new genus of stick insect from Peninsular Malaysia (Insecta: Phasmida: Pseudophasmatidae). *Mal. Nat. Journ.* 49: 29–33.

——————— (1995c). An introduction to the world of stick and leaf-insects. *Insect World International* 1: 25–7.

——————— (1996). Changes of taxonomy in giant stick insects. *Phasmid Studies* 5: 25–31.

——————— (1999). *Stick-insects of Peninsular Malaysia and Singapore.* Malaysian Nature Society, Kuala Lumpur.

Brock, P.D. & Seow-Choen, F. (1995). Notes on the stick insect genus *Abrosoma* in Peninsular Malaysia (Insecta: Phasmida) including the description of a new species. *Mal. Nat. Journ.* 49: 19–27.

Brock, P.D. & Seow-Choen, F. (2000). The Stick Insects (Insecta: Phasmida) of Hong Kong. *Serangga* 5: 115–147.

Brunner von Wattenwyl, K. (1893). Revision du systeme des Orthopteres et description des especes rapportees par M. Leonardo Fea de Birmanie. *Annali del Museo Civico di Storia Naturale "G. Doria" Genova* (2)13: 1–130.

Brunner von Wattenwyl, K. & Redtenbacher, J. (1906–08). *Insektenfamilie der Phasmiden.* Leipzig. Engelmann Verlag.

Burmeister, H. (1838). *Handbuch der Entomologie* Vol 2. TCF Enslin, Berlin.

Chan, C.L. & Lee, S.W. (1994). The thorny tree-nymph stick insect *Heteropteryx dilatata* of Peninsular Malaysia. *Mal. Nat. Journ.* 48: 5–6.

Fabricius, J.C. (1793). *Entomologia systematica emendata et aucta.* Orthopt Vol. II, Havniae.

————— (1798). *Supplementum Entomologiae Systematicae.*

Gray, G.R. (1832). In: Griffith, E. *The Animal Kingdom, arranged in conformity with its organisation by the Baron Cuvier. Insecta* Vol 2. Whittaker, Treacher, and Co., London.

————— (1835). *Synopsis of the species of insects belonging to the family Phasmidae.* Longman, Rees, Ormes, Brown, Green and Longman. London.

————— (1843). Description of several species of *Phyllium . Zoologists* 1: 117–23.

de Haan, W. (1842). *Bijdragen tot de kennis der Orthoptera.* In: Temminck, C.L. Verhandelingen over de natuurlijke Geschiedenis der Nederlandsche overzeesche Bezittingen, Vol. 2. Leiden.

Hausleithner, B. (1984). Eine neue *Phyllium*-art aus Malaysia (Phasmatodea: Phyllidae). *Entomologische Zeitschrift* 94: 39–43.

Karny, H.H. (1923). Zur Nomenklatur der Phasmoiden. *Treubia* 3: 130–42.

Kiew, R. & Seow-Choen, F. (2000). Stick-insects destroying orchids. *Gardenwise* 14: 24.

Kirby, W.F. (1904). *A synonymic catalogue of orthoptera, Vol. 1. Orthoptera, Euplexoptera, Cursoria et Grescoria (Forficulidae, hemimeridae, Blattidae, Mantidae, Phasmidae).* Longman & Co., London.

Kitchener, H.J. (1960). The giant stick insect—*Eurycnema goliath*-Gray. *Mal. Nat. Journ.* 14: 147–51.

Linnaeus, C. (1758). *Systema Naturae per regna tria naturae secondum classes, ordines, genera, species, cum characteribus, differentiis, synonymis, locis.* Ex X (I0. Laurentii Salvii, Holmiae.

Nadchatram, M. (1963). The winged stick insect, *Eurycnema versifasciata* Serville (Phasmida, Phasmidae) with special reference to its life history. *Mal. Nat. Journ.* 17: 33–40.

Parkinson, J. (1798). Description of the *Phasma dilatatum. Trans. Linn. Soc. Lond.* (1)4: 190–192.

Rabenstein, R. & Hausleithner, B. (1998). Fressen und gefressen werden: Freiland beobachtungen zur Ernahrung und zu Pradatoren von Phasmiden im Gombak-Tal (W-Malaysia) (Phasmida:heteronemiidae, Phasmatidae, Pseudophasmatidae). *Mitt. Internat. Entomol. Ver.* 23: 1–12.

Ridley, H.N. (1894). Stick-insects destroying orchids. *Journ. Str. Br. Roy. As. Soc.* 26: 204.

de Saussure, H. (1868). Phasmidarum novarum nonnullae. *Revue et Magasin de Zoologie Pue et Appliquee* 20: 63–70.

Seow-Choen, F. (1993a). The dangers of using head torches in the tropics. *The Phasmid Study Group* 56: 6.

————— (1993b). Colour of newly hatched *Phyllium. The Phasmid Study Group* 56:7.

————— (1993c). *Datames oileus* and bramble. *The Phasmid Study Group* 56: 7.

————— (1993d). Guava and stick and leaf-insects. *The Phasmid Study Group* 58; 9–10.

————— (1993e). A stick insect year in Singapore. *The Phasmid Study Group* 58: 9–10.

————— (1995a). Walking Leaves. *Nature Watch* 3: 16–19.

——————— (1995b). The longest insect in the world: *Pharnacia serratipes. Malayan Naturalist:* 48: 12.

——————— (1995c). Two more gynandromorphs of the Malayan Jungle Nymph, *Heteropteryx dilatata* (Phasmida) with notes on captive behaviour. *Bull. Am. Ent. Soc.* 54: 49–51.

——————— (1995d). The stick insect *Datames oileus* (Westwood) 1859 (Phasmida) *Bull. Am. Ent. Soc.* 54: 239.

——————— (1996a). Reproductive behaviour in stick insects. *Insect and Invertebrate World* 1: 23–25.

——————— (1996b). Leaf insects of Peninsular Malaysia. *Nature Malaysiana* 21: 68–73.

——————— (1997a). Stick Insects. *Malayan Naturalist* 51: 32–33.

——————— (1997b). *A Guide to the Stick and Leaf Insects of Singapore.* Singapore Science Centre 1997.

——————— (1998). *Pharnacia chiniensis*, n. sp., A new species of stick-insect from Peninsular Malaysia (Phasmida: Phasmatidae). *Serangga* 3: 183–9.

——————— (2000). Illustrated guide and key to the *Haaniella* (Phasmida: Bacillidae: Heteroteryginae) species of Malaysia. *Serangga* 5: 149–164.

Seow-Choen. F. & Brock, P.D. (1996). A rare stick insect from Singapore, *Lopaphus brachypterus* (de Haan) 1842 with description of the male and egg. *Bull. Am. Ent. Soc.* 55: 79–82.

Seow-Choen, F., Brock, P.D. & Seow-En, I. (1994a). The Stick-Insects of Singapore. *Singapore Scientists* 70: 10–14.

——————— (1994b). Nates on the Stick-insect *Prisomera malaya* (Stål) (Phasmida) in Singapore with a description of the male and egg. *Mal. Nat. Journ.* 48: 59–64.

——————— (1994c). Colour variations of the stick insect *Necroscia roseipennis* Serville (Phasmida=Phasmatodea) in Singapore. *Bull. Am. Ent. Soc.* 53: 71–73.

——————— I (1994d). An introduction to the stick and leaf insects of Singapore. *Malay Naturalist* 46: 7–11.

Seow-Choen, F. & Goh, Y.Y. (1999). New records of stick insects from Pulau Tioman, Peninsular Malaysia including description of a new species of *Abrosoma* (Phasmida: Pseudophasmatidae: Aschiphasmatinae). *Raffles Bull. Zool.* 6: 263–9.

Seow-Choen, F. & Seow-En I (1994). Nature's Mimics. *Nature Malaysiana* 19: 89–96.

Seow-Choen F, Seow-En, I. & Seow-An, S. (1996). Colour in stick and leaf insects. *Nature Malaysiana* 21: 40–47.

Seow-Choen, F., Tay, E.P., Brock, P.D. & Seow-En, I. (1994). Foodplants of some stick insects (Phasmida=Phasmatodea) from Singapore. *Mal. Nat. Journ.* 47: 393–6.

Stål, C. (1875). *Recensio Orthopterorum. Revue critique des Orthopteres decrits par Linne, de Geer et Thunberg.* Vol. 3: 4–105. PA Norstedt & Soner, Stockholm.

Tay, E.P. & Seow-Choen, F. (1996). Relationship of Plant Families and Stick-Insects in Peninsular Malaysia and Singapore. *Biodiversity and the Dynamics of Ecosystems. DIWPA Series* 1: 181–190.

Westwood, J.O. (1830). Insectorum Arachnoidemque novorum Decades duo. *Zoo. Journ. Lond.* 5: 442–3.

——————— (1848). *The Cabinet of Oriental Entomology.* London.

——————— (1859). *Catalogue of the orthopterous insects in the collection of the British Museum. Part 1. Phasmidae.* London.

Acknowledgements

This book would not have been possible except for the help and encouragement of friends and family. My wife, Ching Peng have had to endure long nights where our children; Isaac Seow-En, Samuel Seow-An and Olivia Seow-Wen; and I have left her alone at home and in hotel rooms to look for phasmids. My family have also had to holiday only where phasmids could be found and this book is really due to their endurance in accompanying me to those places.

Mr Chan Chew Lun (Kota Kinabalu, Sabah), a fellow phasmid enthusiast has been a constant source of inspiration. Mr Yong Ket Hyun kindly prepared the map and Mr Cheng Jen Wai was responsible for the design and layout.

Mr Paul D. Brock (Slough, England) who as I have mentioned in my first book has been a mentor as well as friend in my phasmid studies and has never been stingy in sharing his vast knowledge of phasmids.

Ms Lee Su Win (Tapah), a nature lover and friend has been very helpful in ferrying me around phasmid areas as well as in her generous hospitality thus allowing me, my phasmid hunts at night. Mr David Goh and Mr B.T. Chin (Penang Butterfly Farm) have been very enthusiastic towards my research and have generously supplied specimens that I have needed. I wish also to record herein their genuine interest in the conservation of West Malaysian insects and wish them all the best in their public education programmes. Mr Michael Yeh (Ipoh) has also been of great help in supplying phasmids. I would also like to record my sincere appreciation to Dr Laurence Kirton (Entomologist, Foresst Research Institute Malaysia, Kepong), Datuk Dr Salleh Mohamed Nor (Malaysian Nature Society), Prof Mohamed Salleh Mohamedsaid (Universiti Kebangsaan Malaysia, Bangi) for their encouragement and permission to collect in various places in West Malaysia.

I would also like to record my sincere appreciation to the Managers and Executive Director of the National Parks Board, Singapore for permission to collect and study phasmids in Singapore. It has also been a great blessing to work with Mr Tay Eng Pin (formerly of the Singapore Botanic Gardens) and staff of the Singapore Herbarium in the identification of phamid foodplants. Last but not least, I would like to thank all my friends and colleagues especially those in Les Laboratoires Servier and Ethicon Endosurgery who have arranged and often accompanied me on my wild insect hunts late at night all over West Malaysia.

Index

170

Other titles by *Natural History Publications (Borneo)*

For more information, please contact us at

Natural History Publications (Borneo) Sdn. Bhd.
A913, 9th Floor, Wisma Merdeka
P.O. Box 13908, 88846 Kota Kinabalu, Sabah, Malaysia
Tel: 088-233098 Fax: 088-240768 e-mail: chewlun@tm.net.my

Mount Kinabalu: Borneo's Magic Mountain—an introduction to the natural history of one of the world's great natural monuments *by* K.M. Wong & C.L. Chan

Enchanted Gardens of Kinabalu: A Borneo Diary *by* Susan M. Phillipps

A Colour Guide to Kinabalu Park *by* Susan K. Jacobson

Kinabalu: The Haunted Mountain of Borneo *by* C.M. Enriquez (Reprint)

National Parks of Sarawak *by* Hans P. Hazebroek and Abang Kashim Abg. Morshidi

A Walk through the Lowland Rainforest of Sabah *by* Elaine J.F. Campbell

In Brunei Forests: An Introduction to the Plant Life of Brunei Darussalam
      by K.M. Wong (Revised edition)

The Larger Fungi of Borneo *by* David N. Pegler

Pitcher-plants of Borneo *by* Anthea Phillipps & Anthony Lamb

Nepenthes of Borneo *by* Charles Clarke

Nepenthes of Sumatra and Peninsular Malaysia *by* Charles Clarke

The Plants of Mount Kinabalu 3: Gymnosperms and Non-orchid Monocotyledons
      by John H. Beaman & Reed S. Beaman

Slipper Orchids of Borneo *by* Phillip Cribb

The Genus Paphiopedilum (Second edition) *by* Phillip Cribb

The Genus Pleione (Second edition) *by* Phillip Cribb

Gingers of Peninsular Malaysia and Singapore
      by K. Larsen, H. Ibrahim, S.H. Khaw & L.G. Saw

Mosses and Liverworts of Mount Kinabalu
      by Jan P. Frahm, Wolfgang Frey, Harald Kürschner & Mario Manzel

Birds of Mount Kinabalu, Borneo *by* Geoffrey W.H. Davison

The Birds of Borneo (Fourth edition) *by* Bertram E. Smythies (Revised by Geoffrey W.H. Davison)

The Birds of Burma (Fourth edition) *by* Bertram E. Smythies

Proboscis Monkeys of Borneo *by* Elizabeth L. Bennett & Francis Gombek

The Natural History of Orang-utan *by* Elizabeth L. Bennett

The Systematics and Zoogeography of the Amphibia of Borneo *by* Robert F. Inger (Reprint)

A Field Guide to the Frogs of Borneo *by* Robert F. Inger & Robert B. Stuebing

A Field Guide to the Snakes of Borneo *by* Robert B. Stuebing & Robert F. Inger

The Natural History of Amphibians and Reptiles in Sabah *by* Robert F. Inger & Tan Fui Lian

Marine Food Fishes and Fisheries of Sabah *by* Chin Phui Kong

Layang Layang: A Drop in the Ocean *by* Nicolas Pilcher, Steve Oakley & Ghazally Ismail

Phasmids of Borneo *by* Philip E. Bragg

The Dragon of Kinabalu and other Borneo Stories *by* Owen Rutter (Reprint)

Land Below the Wind *by* Agnes N. Keith (Reprint)

Three Came Home *by* Agnes N. Keith (Reprint)

Forest Life and Adventures in the Malay Archipelago *by* Eric Mjöberg (Reprint)

A Naturalist in Borneo *by* Robert W.C. Shelford (Reprint)

Twenty Years in Borneo *by* Charles Bruce (Reprint)

With the Wild Men of Borneo *by* Elizabeth Mershon (Reprint)

Kadazan Folklore (*Compiled and edited by* Rita Lasimbang)

An Introduction to the Traditional Costumes of Sabah (*eds.* Rita Lasimbang & Stella Moo-Tan)

Bahasa Malaysia titles:

Manual latihan pemuliharaan dan penyelidikan hidupan liar di lapangan
     oleh Alan Rabinowitz (*Translated by* Maryati Mohamed)

Etnobotani *oleh* Gary J. Martin (*Translated by* Maryati Mohamed)

Panduan Lapangan Katak-Katak Borneo *oleh* R.F. Inger dan R.B. Stuebing

Other titles available through
Natural History Publications (Borneo)

The Bamboos of Sabah *by* Soejatmi Dransfield

The Morphology, Anatomy, Biology and Classification of Peninsular Malaysian Bamboos
     by K.M. Wong

The Plants of Mount Kinabalu 1: Ferns and Fern Allies *by* B.S. Parris, R.S. Beaman & J.H. Beaman

The Plants of Mount Kinabalu 2: Orchids *by* J.J. Wood, R.S. Beaman & J.H. Beaman

Forests and Trees of Brunei Darussalam (eds. K.M. Wong & A.S. Kamariah)

Rafflesia: Magnificent Flower of Sabah *by* Kamarudin Mat Salleh

The Theory and Application of A Systems Approach to Silvicultural Decision Making
     by Michael Kleine

Orchids of Borneo Vol. 1 *by* C.L. Chan, A. Lamb, P.S. Shim & J.J. Wood

Orchids of Borneo Vol. 2 *by* Jaap J. Vermeulen

Orchids of Borneo Vol. 3 *by* Jeffrey J. Wood

Orchids of Java *by* J.B. Comber

Orchids of Vanuatu *by* B. Lewis & P.J. Cribb

Orchids of the Solomon Islands and Bougainville *by* B.A. Lewis & P.J. Cribb

The Orchids of Madagascar
    by David Du Puy, Phillip Cribb, Jean Bosser, Johan & Clare Hermans

A Checklist of the Orchids of Borneo *by* J.J. Wood & P.J. Cribb

A Field Guide to the Mammals of Borneo *by* Junaidi Payne & Charles M. Francis

Pocket Guide to the Birds of Borneo *Compiled by* Charles M. Francis

The Fresh-water Fishes of North Borneo *by* Robert F. Inger & Chin Phui Kong

The Exploration of Kina Balu *by* John Whitehead

Kinabalu: Summit of Borneo (eds. K.M. Wong & A. Phillipps)

Common Seashore Life of Brunei *by* Marina Wong & Aziah binte Hj. Ahmad

Birds of Pelong Rocks *by* Marina Wong & Hj. Mohammad bin Hj. Ibrahim

Ants of Sabah *by* Arthur Y.C. Chung

Traditional Stone and Wood Monuments of Sabah *by* Peter Phelan

Borneo: the Stealer of Hearts *by* Oscar Cooke (1991 Reprint)

Maliau Basin Scientific Expedition (eds. Maryati Mohamed, Waidi Sinun, Ann Anton, Mohd. Noh
    Dalimin & Abdul-Hamid Ahmad)

Tabin Scientific Expedition
    (eds. Maryati Mohamed, Mahedi Andau, Mohd. Nor Dalimin & Titol Peter Malim)

Traditional Cuisines of Sabah

Cultures, Costumes and Traditions of Sabah, Malaysia: An Introduction

Tamparuli Tamu: A Sabah Market *by* Tina Rimmer